Beyond Soundings

BEYOND SOUNDINGS

BY

ROBERT LLOYD PRAEGER
D. Sc.

THE TALBOT PRESS LIMITED
DUBLIN & CORK

FIRST PUBLISHED 1930

PRINTED IN IRELAND
AT THE TALBOT PRESS
DUBLIN

NOTE

The majority of these sketches appeared
in the *Irish Statesman* during the last
five years, a few in *The Garden*, one in
the *Cornhill Magazine*; several are un-
published previously.   To the Editors
of the journals named I am indebted for
permission to reprint them.

R. Ll. P.

19 FITZWILLIAM SQUARE,
    DUBLIN.

CONTENTS

BEYOND SOUNDINGS

THE FAIRY RING

SHE was a very old woman—ninety-six years of age, she said. Her white hair, parted in the middle, hung down her back, like a child's; the brightness that still gleamed in her eyes was only partly concealed by old horn spectacles, long since bereft of their stays, and tied round her head with a piece of string. Her face had the far-away look of one who has seen much, and who still sees things that are hidden from the telephone-racked and motor-haunted modern. She sat in the spring sunshine in front of her thatched house among the Tyrone hills, and spoke to us of the fairy folk, the " good people" who dwell in rath and mound, mostly unseen but ever present, and strangely tolerant of the newer race who have usurped their old-time kingdom—but tolerant only so long as the conventions are observed, and due respect shown towards the ancient régime. If a new house is to be built, you must take care not to trespass on " gentle " ground. In the evening you plant a post at each of the four corners of the site. If these are still standing in the morning, all is well; but if one or more is down, you

9

know you are on forbidden land, and if you are wise you will choose a different spot. The fairy paths that cross and re-cross the hills also, are not for mortal use. If you walk on them, you will lose all sense of direction, and wander forlorn; nor will the spell be removed till you have stripped off your clothes, and put them on inside out. She told us how, as a young woman, she used to go at dawn to attend to the cattle. Frequently she would hear fairy music, and stealing up, would see the " loghery men " assembling at the fairy ring. " How are you, Pat," " How are you, Mike," they would call. Then they would dance together in the magic circle. " Throw up the cap, throw up the cap," they would shout, and all would toss their red caps into the air. She stopped, and her thin hands moved to an unheard melody. A curlew out on the bog raised his tremulous breeding-note, and from the main road across the valley a motor hooted in reply. One morning, she said, she had seen near the old thorn a little man dancing, dancing, dancing. He wore knee-breeches tied with bright ribbons, and as he danced, the ribbons whirled round and round. He saw her and shouted " Hello, hello!" But she was frightened, and ran home. Later in the day she picked up courage and returned to the place, and where he had danced she found on the grass his little pipe. She kept it always safe: and now she called to a great-grandchild in the house to bring out her work-box. But, alas! she searched for the pipe in vain; and she lamented over the graceless younger generation, who have no respect for the aged, and no reverence for the older things. As we followed the field-track that led towards the road, we looked with less unseeing eyes at the dark green circle on the grass and the two ancient thorns rising from their pile of stones.

* * * * *

Among the jetsam cast up by the post on my table is a grey slab of paper, half covered with a wrapper bearing an American stamp. " Fungus Fairy Rings in Eastern Colorado and their effect on Vegetation " the legend reads; and underneath I catch the name H. L. Shantz. At once there comes to my mind a desolate scene—a wide landscape of snow-fields rising in low, swelling domes, with the lovely blue of glacier ice showing through where a steeper slope ruffles the surface, and bare, broad, rocky hills, and lakes in which little icebergs move like stately swans. Among the rocks nestle a hundred unfamiliar flowers, hurrying to complete in two brief months, on this Norwegian roof of the world, their annual life-cycle. And high up on the great glacier is Shantz, a speck against the snow, busily collecting in glass tubes icy specimens to be examined for those minute plants which maintain existence among the snow crystals; for nowhere on the surface of our planet, from the Pole itself to the deepest abyss of the ocean, is life wholly absent ... The scene changes abruptly; we are in the lounge of a fashionable hotel at Lugano, gorgeous and hideous, on a scorching August day; and a merry party of botanists is enjoying the spectacle of Shantz, in shirt and knickers, in vigorous argument with a

horror-stricken major-domo, who would fain con-
vince him of the blasphemy of entering the sacro-
sanct luncheon-room in that ungodly costume.

But what has Shantz to tell us about fairy rings?
Here we find the whole matter duly set forth in
American type and precise, dispassionate, scientific
language. Fairy rings by the hundred he and his
co-worker have measured and sectioned and
analysed with the aid of microscope and test-tube,
biological literature has been ransacked, and we
have before us an apotheosis of the Fairy Ring,
Elfdans, Rond de Sorcière, Duivelstjeinpad, Danse
de Fées, Hexentanzplatz, or whatever we may choose
to call it. We gather at once that, as is well known,
these rings are associated with the growth of certain
toadstools, and furthermore, that not one but at
least fifty different kinds of those higher mushroom-
like fungi with which we are all familiar, take part
in their production. But we are made to realise
that a fungus plant consists not solely or even mainly
of the toadstool which is so familiar an object in
field and wood. The plant is formed essentially of
many thread-like filaments growing and spreading
some inches down in the soil, where it feeds on the
humus or decayed vegetable matter which the soil
contains. And just as water-plants which creep on
the bottom of pools or lakes send up their blossoms
into the air, so the fungus, when it produces what
corresponds to flowers, raises them above the surface of the ground, and this fruiting part is what
we call a toadstool. The young fungus plant, starting life, sends out its threadlike branches in all

directions. These exhaust the humus-food as they grow, continually extend outwards seeking new supplies, and die out behind, thus tending to form a ring of increasing diameter. The mass of fungus threads—or mycelium, to use the technical term— is remarkably impenetrable to water, with the result that in dry countries a ring of starved or even dead grass is often produced on the surface above it. But in the older part, the inner section of the ring, the effect of the activities of fungus growth and of the subsequent decay of the mycelium is to produce nitrates and salts of ammonia, invaluable food for the plants of the pasture, with the result that here we get a stimulated zone, where the grass is more vigorous and greener than elsewhere. Thus the fairy ring is formed, expanding at the rate of about a foot a year as the fungus extends its growth, continuing to spread it may be for half a century or more, eventually breaking up through contact with unfavourable ground or other causes. And so, with much minute observation, chemical analysis, and technical discussion, does Wizard Shantz produce, develop, and eventually disperse, his fairy ring.

*   *   *   *   *

One evening I lay at sundown on the edge of a rath high up on the Clare hills, with the dim green circles of the fairy rings staining the slope below. My companion, a mountainy man from Lough Graney, most desolate of Irish lakes, finished his tale—a startling one, concerning the fate of two men who cut down a fairy thorn; how one of them went out to a rock projecting over the lake, when a great hand, all scaly like a fish, rose out of the water and enveloped him, and hand and victim vanished without a sound. And how the other was walking along the road near his own house, and a woman neighbour only a few perches behind him, when suddenly the road opened, and he was gone; and when they searched, they found only a little white heap like flour on the spot where he had disappeared for ever. The voice of the teller ceased, and silence fell between us. Save for the distant gurgle of a nightjar, like a rivulet dripping in a mossy hollow, the stillness was absolute. All nature paused under the spell of that magic sunset. The swelling mass of Slieve Barnagh behind us cut off the brighter light, and the Shannon lay in shadow; but beyond the river, the high hills over by Silvermines glowed rosy purple, and above the towering bulk of Slieve Kimalta a little fiery cloud hung suspended, like a hand laid in benediction on the mountain's head. To the left, Lough Derg, slate patched with pale yellow, stretched its sinuous length, and beyond it, dim and mysterious, the limestone plain extended to an infinitely far horizon of silver and grey. An enchanted land, fit for fairies and dreamers.

But away to the right a constellation of flashing blue-white electric lamps, far-flung over the valley, columns of dark smoke and wavering jets of steam, show where the German engineers, backed by some thousand Irishmen, are tearing open the solid earth and smashing through the solid rock to change the course of the Shannon. Titanic excavators drag down the hills, tons at a time. Huge cranes clatter, engines shriek, and the boom of heavy explosions shakes the air. Ghostly walls of white concrete rise, pipes as large as railway tunnels; and in tall buildings glittering machinery stands, which will flash, along far-flung tingling spider-lines, scintillating light and shattering power to every corner of the land. Is not this also magic—mere wizardry in a modern manifestation? What they could not explain, our fathers termed magic or miracle; what we can explain—or think we can—we term science. But the miracle of yesterday is the science of to-day. Everything supernatural is natural, and everything natural is supernatural. It depends merely on how we attune our minds towards the million mysteries that beset us on every side, an encompassing magic circle, a fairy ring in very truth. Our autogyros and thermionic valves and wireless portraits and gyrostatic compasses and hundred-thousand-volt transmission lines—what are they but the latest pranks played on us, in this Midsummer Night's Dream of an existence, by Puck and Merlin and the Klaboterman—re-incarnated if you like, as Marconi and Edison and Joseph John Thompson (strange name for a magician!); and the fairies must laugh over the ponderous polysyllabic words with which we endeavour to explain the unexplained forces which they use for their magic. So, while it may be that our fairy ring spread upon the meadow is merely a necessary result of increase in the available nitrogenous content of the soil due to the progressive growth of Agaricus, Calvatia and other Basidiomycetes, it still remains a manifestation of that greatest magic of all, which we call Life; and who shall blame us if we choose to view the mystery in another way, and to think that still

> Round the fairy grass ring frolic elf and fay
> In Sherwood, in Sherwood, about the break of day.

*   *   *   *   *

To-day we knock electrons off an atom as easily as Newton might have knocked apples off an apple-tree, or man of the Neolithic time chips off a piece of flint, though that electron is a million times beyond the limit of vision of the most powerful ultra-microscope; we send sound and sight flying round the world at will. To-morrow we may be producing the mystery that we call Life out of dead matter, or destroying matter itself in order to utilise it, in the form of energy, for our petty needs—we, microscopic crawlers on an inconsiderable satellite of a petty and dying star—our Sun—itself a negligible item of a universe vast beyond realisation, yet infinite neither in space nor time, but tending inevitably towards a known end, though its beginning remains wrapped in profoundest mystery. The day after to-morrow? Perhaps the enfolding curtains of space and time themselves, those " illusory appearances," will be torn asunder, and the mind of man, naked, still groping forward, will stand face to face with—what?

ISLAND MEMORIES.

Islands are always fascinating—particularly if they are small. Their aloofness makes a curious appeal. To reach them we must cross water—a capricious medium of many moods. One rambles over them with a not unpleasing sense of restriction; the constant presence of a circumambient sea is stimulating; and the ships which sail upon it acquire a new significance, from the fact that their ministrations are essential if our sojourn is not to be prolonged indefinitely. Picture the romance of approaching, after days of unbroken horizon, an unknown island! We cannot hope for this in our prosaic latitudes, but, all the same the most fascinating holiday that our own country offers is, to my mind, a sojourn on one or other of the little islets that lie off the Irish coast.

I remember as a boy charging boldly down on the Copelands amid swirling tides and wreaths of fog; finding Mew Island more by accident than design, and visiting its wonderful tern colonies; and how thankful we were when tide-rips and mist were safely left behind. Fog also dominated a visit to the savage rock-shelf of Tory, when our little steamer groped her way on and on till voices, coming apparently from the sky, told us that we were right under the cliffs—a risky quest with half a hundred holiday-makers on board and a captain who did not know the coast. We explored the island in blinding, drifting sea-mist, amid the wailing of befogged destroyers; then groped our way back till we butted into Horn Head, where we had to anchor for the night, with no food and no beds. But this was preferable to rough days on the crowded little tub bound for Aran, when passengers, live stock, and the very kegs and barrels were sea-sick, and deplorable pessimism prevailed. But why dwell on the exceptions? These island crossings were for the greater part among the most exhilarating things in life. Who would not wish to find himself at dawn on a June morning in the rushing tide that eddies between Rathlin and Ballycastle, with Fair Head rising like a black wedge to the eastward, and the sunrise coming up over the Scottish islands? Or in a dancing curragh on the Sound between Dunmore Head and the towering mass of the Great Blasket? The Sound is full of fish, and hundreds of gannets, from their breeding haunt on the Skelligs, are at work. They dash down as thick as hail-stones, and the blue water boils with their commotion. Then there was one really exciting crossing to Clare Island. I think our boatmen did not realise how bad the weather was, or they would not have ventured out. But once clear of Achill Sound there was no turning back, and we staggered under a rag of sail along gigantic rollers a quarter of a mile from crest to crest, now lashed with spray on the top of a wave, now sinking into the shelter of the deep troughs, now running for it under bare poles when a squall burst down, and the rollers threatened to comb.

There was a burning afternoon too when our hooker

lay becalmed between Inisheer and the towering
Cliffs of Moher, while Aran lay like a grey cloud,
and our sails flapped helplessly in the oily, lumpy
swell, and the boat groaned, and we solaced ourselves with fresh caught mackerel still more freshly
fried, while George Francis Fitzgerald discoursed
on the mechanics of the universe, and Rudolphe
Christen sketched us one by one.

But what of the islands themselves? They are full
of beauty and interest. There are few that do not
harbour the remains of ancient monasteries and
churches (for the early Irish ecclesiastics had a rare
taste for solitude), and of strongholds very much
older than these. Then the bird life in summer is a
perpetual joy. The smaller creatures, too, and the
plants have a peculiar interest, for one is always
puzzling over the problem as to whether they came
across the water, or whether they have survived
since that distant time when the islands formed part
of the mainland. I was on the Great Saltee once
with a lively party of naturalists. The ages of three
of them, I remember, made a total of 215 years,
which says much for the healthiness of biological
pursuits. We slept on the floor of a ruined house
with half a roof (the only building on the island) and
wandered about by day and night studying birds
and flowers. But one morning there was trouble
—a bullock was missing. Had we killed and eaten
it? It was a relief when next day it was found in its
old home on the Little Saltee, two miles to the
northward. The intelligent beast had chosen the
flood tide for his swim, for had he started on the

ebb—he might have made Waterford Haven, or he might not! The Saltees are an ideal place for the study of bird life, for the islands are so low that one can walk everywhere through the teeming colonies. The birds are exceptionally tame also, being carefully protected; you can sidle up to a guillemot and, stretching a cautious arm, stroke its head before it decides to fly off. Different are the great bird colonies on cliff-bound fastnesses like Clare Island, where the rows of tiny white dots that stand for puffins, razorbills, guillemots, and gulls rise tier upon tier to a height of a thousand feet, absolutely unapproachable. In contrast to this, memories come of low, gravelly islands in Strangford Lough, in June alive with nesting birds. One sailed from islet to islet, to be met at each by the shrieks of a white cloud of terns, the clamour of gulls, the sharp cry of the oyster-catcher. The fringe of grass-wrack that marks storm-level would be so thickly sown with eggs that one had to pick one's steps. The ringed plovers chose little hollows in the shingle, where their mottled eggs were generally accompanied by a few bright shells, daintily disposed; the oyster-catchers preferred the gravelly points; the red-breasted mergansers were further in, amid the coarse grass, where they crouched over their numerous brood till one almost stepped on them; and all around were the waveless waters of the land-locked lough, reflecting the fertile undulating fields of Down. Other pleasant pictures crowd up—a clear lakelet on Inishturk, set in wind-shorn heather and full of the delicate blossoms of the water lobelia;

the glorious sea-cliff of Clare Island, cushioned with alpine plants; a rock on Lambay, on which one lay very still, surrounded by great grey seals, which sprawled so close that one could look into their clear brown eyes, and note the tiny ear-holes on the sides of the head. But the scene that most sticks in my mind is a widely different one—an angry foam-flecked sea, low-flying cloud and driving rain, the wind howling in the rigging; in the midst of that desolate waste of waters, a single lonely pinnacle of stone, like a haycock canted over by the wind, and not much bigger, seemingly. It is Rockall, the most isolated speck of rock in the world, which we have come four hundred miles to see. The great rollers rave around its base, sending now and again fountains of spray right over it. Great shearwaters flash by on wings bent like a bow, and stormy petrels flirt along the waves, just touching the foam with their dainty feet. It is comfortless on the bridge, but in the deck-house a jolly company is assembled: there are W. S. Green, R. M. Barrington, Harvey-Brown, De Vismes Kane, Lyster Jameson—alas! how many men have made their last voyage: these good companions are all now gone. But the islands are there still, untouched by recent troubles, untainted by the reek of petrol, as populous as ever with birds and flowers. Long may they remain " uncivilised "!

THE MORNING MAIL.

THE motor-horn toots impatiently, and we stumble
down the narrow stair and out under the glowing
bougainvillea which roofs the back yard, to where
the " correo " stands throbbing at the door. The
sun is not yet up; but the light is clear and cold. It
is carnival time, and the empty streets have that
dishevelled look that follows a night of dissipation.
Our fellow-travellers make room for us with cheerful
Spanish greetings—countrywomen in spotless white
and yellow skirts and kerchiefs, strayed revellers
with faces and clothes daubed with scented powder,
a venerable cura going to celebrate Mass in an out-
lying church, a gendarme in grey and yellow uniform,
very smart and alert, an old woman with a kid in
her arms. Our baggage is added to the numberless
packages which already festoon the 'bus—mud-
guards, running-board, and roof. " Anda," cries the
conductor, resplendent in a new shoulder-bag; a
handcuffed cock on the roof utters a despairing
crow; and with a jerk we are off. As we leave the
town the sun peeps above the gigantic precipice of
Time—four thousand feet of dark basalt, velvet-black
in the shadow—and golden light floods across the
lovely valley in which Los Llanos lies. The eye ranges
over miles of flowering fruit-trees—almonds, peaches,
nectarines, pears; grey fig-trees, still leafless; red-tiled
cottages buried in flowers of a hundred kinds; and,
like the skeleton at the feast, belts of jagged dark

lava, a reminder of how all this fertility began, and of how it yet may end. The sunlight is switched off again as we get under the main ridge of the island, and all is blue shadow, for Palma rises from the ocean like the high-pitched roof of a cathedral: the February wind blows keen. "Mucho frio" the cotton-clad revellers shiver, and try to wrap themselves in the flapping curtains. There is an interlude while we pause to take on board a stout dame accompanied by a grave and patriarchal goat. The goat is very polite, but becomes suddenly panic-stricken, and a general melée ensues before it is safely bestowed on the front seat beside the driver. We leave the valley of almond blossom behind, and pass into a land more recently emerged from the throes of vulcanism, with shattered craters, red, yellow and purple, raising gaunt crags to right and left, and cinder fields full of twisted leafless vines. Car-loads of noisy revellers in absurd costumes dash past, discharging broadsides of confetti and scented powder. The carratera (carriage-road) crosses frightful lava-flows, coal-black, rugged, like cascades suddenly frozen solid; they descend from the pine-clad heights three thousand feet above, and writhe down the steep slope to where the Atlantic stretches far below, a great blue plain. Across the lavas, pipes of galvanised iron straggle incongruously like stray strands of spider-web, and one can hear the swish of the clear cold water that they convey from distant mountain springs to the thirsty waterless lands beneath. One might write a parable on the queer contrast—this grim burnt-out product of vulcanism, lifeless, hideous, the quintessence of nature in her most terrifying and savage mood, and these silver spider-lines, life-giving, healing, by means of which puny man restores to the hungry earth its fair mantle of greenery, which the fire-demon, acting through both terrestrial and solar heat, has for a while destroyed. Between the streams of lava are grassy glades full of six-foot asphodel, tall and stately, and fields of fragrant lupins, set in purple bugloss—loveliest of all the lovely Canarian weeds. Here and there crouch ancient fig-trees, silver-stemmed, wide-spreading; their branches arch over from the centre, and meeting the ground in a wide circle send up again into the air a ring of smaller branches, so that the whole resembles a gigantic low fountain with a fringe of spray. At a little church hard by the road our cura dismounts, his broad hat and long black cloak still dotted with confetti, and three children come forward shyly to greet him.

Now we enter forest formed of Canary pine, one of the grandest of its noble family; a tree capable of attaining huge dimensions, with great gnarled limbs, and foot-long needles, very slender and of a delicate green, giving to the tree a soft hazy effect that is very lovely. The road winds on in cool shadow. Here we are high over the ocean, its roaring fringe of breakers reduced to a narrow white hem. We are told that so steep is the slope that the wood-cutters have merely to push the logs over the edge of the road, and they roll down to the beach nearly three thousand feet beneath. A delay enables us to walk forward for a while along the still deserted road. The solemn pines, full of singing canaries, rise like columns from steep slopes of black cinders. The sun catches their soft green tops and brown trunks, and by contrast the ground looks like rich black velvet.

A gaping ebony crater, sulphur-streaked, below the road heralds our approach to Fuencaliente, and as we round the sharp southern end of the island we emerge into brilliant sunlight, most welcome after twenty miles of morning shadow. The place derives its name from a hot spring of high medicinal value, once much frequented, which vanished amid the throes of an eruption two centuries ago. In the straggling village hot coffee awaits us, and is gulped down eagerly: news is exchanged; passengers come and go; additions are made to the bags of mail which hang like a cluster of grapes at either side of the wind-screen; the goat dismounts with dainty steps and browses on the roadside flowers. Our driver swaggers out, wiping his mouth, and we are off again—northward now, up the sunny eastern side of the island. The pines are thinner here, and everywhere over the cinder slopes are the black snake-like stems of vines breaking into leaf. There is now a warm glow in the air: it is going to be a hot day. We pass into a region where wide lava-flows occupy the whole ground from mountain-top to ocean. It is two hundred years since the last eruptions took place, but the dark twisted rock is still almost entirely bare; only a small sempervivum, with scarlet stems and golden bloom, gives a note of cheer. The scene changes again in a few miles, and once more we are among fields and houses. The cottages are smothered in flowers—mounds of heliotrope six feet high, roses of half a hundred sorts, tangles of blue plumbago, datura-trees like great umbrellas thickly hung with foot-long white trumpets; the scent of blossoms is overpowering. In the thin corn, all decked with pink convolvulus and blue bugloss, quails are twittering; hoopoes dash in curiously reckless flight across the road, or hoot at us their hollow triple call, which sounds like one piece of hardwood struck thrice against another. Eastward the sunshine glitters on a great expanse of ocean, and Tenerife, a hundred miles away, lies like a dream on the horizon, its famous Peak towering far above the belt of snowy island-cloud. Near by, the northern view opens out to where, beyond the ancient volcano which looks down on it, Santa Cruz de la Palma glitters white on the edge of the sea. Geraniums are planted along the roadside here, apparently by way of hedge. They form boulder-like masses of greenery a yard high, covered with blossom, white, pink, and scarlet; but as a barrier between the road and the twenty-foot drop on its seaward side they strike one as ineffective. The retaining wall which rises over the left side of the road is buried under cascades of mesembryanthemum and orange cassia and roses without end; white lilies and red amaryllis nod at us over its top. The older houses, long and low, with dark stone walls and red tiles, tone well into the landscape of black rock, red earth, gaudy flowers and hot sunlight; but the newer houses are hideous and incongruous to a degree—glaring white cubes, naked and unashamed; prickly pears, with tortuous stems as thick as a man's leg, add to the bizarre effect.

At Breña we take the lower road and sweep down in long zig-zags towards the sea through country half-rock, half-fields. Prickly pears and agaves become numerous, a sure sign of increasing human traffic. The pines, fruit-trees, and grain of the upper levels give way to a monotonous region of banana culture —endless yellow walls supporting, tier above tier, flat irrigated fields filled with the stumpy palm-like stems and heavy tattered dark green foliage of that plant to which so much of the present prosperity of the Canary Islands is due. As we approach the metropolis we are once more reminded that it is carnival. Among the countrywomen bound for the market, carrying on their heads enormous loads of fruit and vegetables, eggs and goat's-milk cheeses, are gay groups of girls hurrying townwards, and again we come within the range of reckless motors with batteries of white powder and scent and confetti. The air is filled with laughter and singing and shouting. We run along half a mile of beach, where the rollers foam over black sand, charge through the long tunnel which carries the road through the precipitous wall of the Caldereta, and at a more sober pace slip past the mole and along the paved length of the crowded Calle O'Daly to our hotel and breakfast.

MORE ISLAND MEMORIES.

JUST at present I am haunted by numberless islands, like W. B. Yeats (though I doubt if I should know a "Danaan shore" if I saw one). In no places that I have been, certainly, have time and sorrow seemed so far away. With the signs of returning spring (I write in March) glimpses of sea and sky keep peeping through; this must be my excuse for coming back to a former theme. Not that our islands are places to fly to for a foretaste of vernal joys. The sea is at its coldest in the early months of the year, and spring delays long. In Achill at Easter it is still winter, and one may gather primroses and hawthorn on northern slopes in Rathlin at the end of July. Often in May, when the plump cattle of Westmeath and Wexford are carousing on fresh-grown grass, the lean beasts on the islands are eking out an iron ration with hay brought from the mainland. I remember a lovely belated spring display of sea-pink and scurvy-grass on the Bills, those lonely stacks away to the south-west of Achill. It is not easy to land here, for on the calmest day the almost imperceptible heave of the Atlantic changes to foaming breakers against the rocks. One chooses a vertical rock-face (with a sufficiency of foot-holds and hand-grips), for there the wave goes straight up and down, and there is no danger of a capsize. Then one notes a niche for one's foot, and steps ashore on the top of a swell. The return is mostly more difficult; some-

times the driest way is to throw one's clothes into the
swaying boat and swim for it. Swimming, indeed,
is the primitive and proper way of approaching an
island.   But, alas! our degenerate bodies refuse
their aid, save to a very limited extent.   I remember
swimming to a rock off Clare Island, among a fleet
of Grey Seals, to discover the identity of a plant
growing on the summit (it proved to be the only
juniper in the district).   The silent presence of those
six-foot carnivores gave one a tingly feeling about
the toes, as they rose up, and looked intently, and
silently sank again.   A more creepy swim was up
the underground river in the Marble Arch caves in
Fermanagh, with a lighted candle stuck in one's cap,
and the water looking like ink, and feeling like ice
—but that is another story.   More heroic was R. J.
Ussher's devotion when he swam to an island (without even a bathing costume) to study a colony of
Roseate Terns, and finding himself confronted on
landing by a tall *chevaux-de-frise* of stinging nettles,
boldly stalked through them to his quarry.

One of the most inspiring spots in Ireland is the
roof-like ridge of the Great Blasket.   An amazing
island this—four miles long, half a mile wide, and a
thousand feet high—a mere knife-edge.   From the
summit of the ridge one can imagine that one could
jump into the Atlantic on either side; and to west
and north and east other fantastic, foam-fringed
islands rise from the blue water, and cliff-walled
headlands.   The Blaskets are especially beloved of
philologists as a sanctuary of our ancient tongue.
We came there in all humility to study, not native

Gaelic, but native plants and animals—which is, after all, an equally legitimate and patriotic pursuit. Hearing that there would be merry-making in the house of the "King" one Sunday afternoon, we returned early to see some Irish dancing.   They *waltzed* to the strains of *The Merry Widow*! When on our return to Dublin we were assailed vigorously for daring to pollute the purity of the shrine by our presence, we listened with a vague bewilderment.

If I wished to show anyone the best thing in Ireland I would take him to Aran. Those grey ledges of limestone, rain-beaten and storm-swept, are different from anything else. The strangeness of the scene, the charm of the people (I don't refer to the rabble that meets the steamer), the beauty of sea and sky, the wealth of both pagan and Christian antiquities, the remarkable vegetation (without a parallel in western Europe save in the adjoining Burren of Clare)—all these help to make a sojourn in Aran a thing never to be forgotten.

Lake islands are especially delightful places—provided they are small enough to escape the attentions of the farmer, for "the world is full of woodmen ... " First, he " clears the ground," and then he comes with cattle, or with ploughs and horses, and all the native flowers and creatures fly before him. In Connemara one may notice that the only trees in the landscape are the wind-shorn thickets on the rocky islets of the lakes. Why? Because only here is there sanctuary. Every tree on the mainland has long since been cut for fuel, and the sheep devour each seedling that appears. But from the islets we

learn what the aboriginal woods consisted of—Oak
and Birch, Holly and Rowan; and underneath their
dense canopy are groves of Foxglove and Cow-
wheat, and sheets of the delicate Filmy Fern. In
Lower Lough Erne, again, there is an archipelago,
of which the smaller islands are quite unspoiled,
covered with trees—which here grow tall, unlike
Connemara—and harbouring a rich undergrowth.
The gravelly beaches too have a brilliant flora of
Harebell and Bedstraw, Golden Rod, Loosestrife,
and fifty other flowers, and ducks and gulls and
terns nest in numbers. Then there are the low
limestone reefs that fill the lakes of the central plain
—Derg and Ree, Corrib, Mask, Carra. The lower
ones, rising barely above flood level, give fascinating
glimpses of undisturbed bird life and plant life. On
the smaller lakes boats are mostly absent, and on
the larger ones they are seldom there when you want
them—so much the better for the birds and flowers.
I recall a stormy day on Lough Corrib; a most
tempting islet only a few hundred yards from shore
—and there, in a tiny cove, a heaven-sent boat, with
a wizened Charon fast asleep in the stern. As it
turned out, he had been too friendly with a whiskey
bottle. He would not row me, but had no objection
to my rowing him. All would have gone well if one
of the crazy oars had not snapped in the rough
water. Charon jumped on the thwart, and the boat
capsized. Proclaiming that he couldn't swim, he
capsized likewise. He proved a heavy tow, and the
jabble made things difficult; both of us were water-
logged and very sad when a particularly hard piece

of the county of Galway hit me in the back. He crawled out and sat on a stone, and cursed me with an intensity of feeling that seemed uncalled for under the circumstances. The islet remains inviolate.

THE MAKING OF IRELAND.

THE study of geology, and of stratigraphical geology in particular, is educative, especially in that it forces our minds away from this all-absorbing Present, including the few thousand years which historians and archæologists call the Past, and causes them to glance along that fragment of the real Past which began with the birth of this world of ours. The study of astronomy provides an equally salutary exercise, with Space added to Time as the medium which our mental telescope must probe; but in descriptive astronomy the figures involved are so gigantic that, however we may strive to grasp them, they remain to a great extent unmeaning. In geology, on the other hand, it is comparatively easy to look back from to-day to that yesterday which saw the birth of the human race, and thence by easy stages through hundreds of such yesterdays to the date of those sediments which contain the earliest known traces of life. That is a quite different thing from the date of the beginning of life, which, for all we can tell, may lie a thousand such yesterdays away from this present, which will be noteworthy to geologists a million years hence as the heyday of Man and Angiosperms, just as Carboniferous times were the heyday of Horsetails, and Jurassic of gigantic Reptiles.

Ireland is an interesting and pleasant place for the study of geological history, for it is built up of rocks representing almost every period recognised by stratigraphers. In other words, at frequent intervals of time (geologically speaking) some portion of that small present land-surface which we call Ireland has been below the sea, or more rarely covered with fresh water, permitting the accumulation of mud or sand, which has survived as slate or limestone or sandstone, to tell us something of the climate and life of the successive ages. One period in particular, the Carboniferous, laid its hand heavily on Ireland. Almost the whole country sank below the sea, and remained there long, while hundreds of feet of limy mud were spread over it. Nothing approaching so general or so prolonged a submergence ever occurred again; all subsequent sedimentation was local and short-lived in comparison, with the result that the surface rocks of Ireland, below the skin of Boulder-clay and peat, from Dublin to Galway and from Armagh to Mallow, still consist mainly of Carboniferous limestone, which is as characteristic of Ireland as its summer greenness or its plethora of public-houses. As regards the deposits of the enormous succeeding period of time, which is known to geologists as Mesozoic, Irish geology had a real stroke of luck. Representatives of all—the Triassic, the Liassic and the Cretaceous—were laid down, at least locally; and comparatively soon afterwards great lava-flows welled forth in the north-east, and, by burying them, protected these beds of chalk, sandstone and shale from the destruction which probably awaited them at the hands of wind, rain, and rivers. For a land-surface connotes a steady wearing-down of its materials, and even the hardest rocks are safe only when buried deep under other rocks; or, better still, below the sea, receiving upon their surface fresh deposits, " the dust of continents to be."

These random thoughts are suggested by the *Handbook to the Geology of Ireland** of Professor Grenville Cole (the latest and final product, alas! of that active brain and busy pen), who has as his colleague in this study of our rocks Mr. T. Hallissy. The main portion of the work saw the light some years ago as a section of the *Handbuch der regionalen Geologie*. The Irish portion, now appearing in the English language, has been revised and enlarged, and provides a succinct epitome of the geology of our island—the only available account, indeed, which includes the results of recent work.

At the outset it is impressed on the reader that the sea which at present surrounds Ireland is a mere temporary film of water, here to-day and gone both yesterday and to-morrow. Ireland has no general geological history apart from western Europe, though local subsidence and elevation have given us more or less than our share of certain rocks—a superfluity of Carboniferous Limestone, for instance, and an unfortunate paucity of the overlying Coal-measures. These latter beds would appear to have been laid down in due course, a gift from the gods, and to have been removed subsequently by denudation, owing to the incurable propensity of Ireland for keeping her head above

* London: T. Murby & Co. 1925.

water. Had she consented to be safely and comfortably buried in post-Carboniferous times, we might now have (which, thank Heaven, we have not!) a second Lancashire where the cattle browse on the Central Plain.

We read also of eras of mountain-building—of the crumpling-up of the earth-rind through the action of mysterious forces. The crumple which raised the ancient mountain-isthmus of Scandinavia had its echo here in the rock-folding of Donegal and Connemara, and a subsequent period of stress gave us Kerry. This was another stroke of luck for Ireland; for without these great buttresses of hard rock to resist the incessant onslaught of the Atlantic, half our country might by this time be below the waves. Is not Hy Brasil now only a myth, and what is left of the once large island of Rockall? Indeed, if one keep one's imagination untrammelled, the romance, the stupendous drama, of our geological history everywhere shines through the set phrases and polysyllabic technical terms of Cole and Hallissy's book. We have dim visions of continents spreading and disappearing, of the rise of great mountain ranges, some still remaining as weathered remnants, some vanished utterly. We see Northern Ireland in the throes of its fire ordeal, with molten lavas welling up and spreading destruction over hundreds of square miles, and rising higher and higher in a great plateau till under its own weight the central part gives way, ultimately to form Lough Neagh and the flowery valley of the Bann. Is it a spark of that Plutonic fire which still glows unquenchable in Belfast? And visions rise of tall forests of impossible trees, tenanted by unthinkable creatures; of vast deserts, embosoming lakes salter than the sea. Lastly, our island vanishes under a ponderous mantle of ice and snow, there to remain for many thousands of years; till after long travail, still staggering from that burden, and still strewn with its débris, it emerges to meet the present, now at length peopled with men and women, and filled with human hopes and aspirations.

CHAHORRA AT HARIA.

WHEN we first saw Haria, from the corkscrew high road which twists to and fro down the precipitous slope which overhangs the town to the southward, it seemed to us a very Garden of Eden. It lay in a hollow among high hills, its white and buff flat-topped houses embowered in tall palms, and embosomed in green fields—actually green fields. We had begun our wanderings through the Canary Islands with the island of Fuerteventura. The southern half of this sixty miles of lava was mere stony desert, across which even our grunting camels complained; it became populous with plants only in the terminal peninsula of Handia, where the ground rises to over two thousand feet. The north-ern half, with its wide stretches of red volcanic soil, ought in March to have been verdant with young crops, but the winter rains had failed, and the rusty soil lay for miles bare of vegetation. Passing on to Lanzarote it had been a relief to see from the steamer a greenish shade over the higher slopes, for that island enjoys a slightly greater rainfall; but the crops were thin and stunted. Accordingly, when we passed the venerated little church of La Virgen de las Niéves, standing lonely on the cliff-edge 2,000 feet above the sea, and saw the oasis of Haria far below us, we welcomed it as a thirsty man might welcome the first glimpse of a cool stream. So far, we had seen verdure only as a concomitant of infrequent irrigation—windmill pumps, little channels leading away from them, and greenery just as far as the channels went. But here were fresh crops without surface water and without pumps—a miracle! The ground which bore them, also, was not red as usual, but velvet black. This was something to be investigated. Our curiosity was not lessened by finding that the black surface was due to cinders. The crops grew in pure fine cinders, as regular in size as if they had been passed through a half-inch sieve. We enquired about the matter. "The chahorra? Come and see." And we were led to a large excavation like a gravel pit. There were our cinders, lying in even sloping layers, bed below bed, to a great depth. Then the mysteries of chahorra cultivation were explained to us. The seeds or young plants are laid or planted in the red volcanic soil, and a four-inch layer of chahorra is then spread over the whole. The chahorra may be in some degree hygroscopic, for according to accounts it not only retains in the soil any moisture which is there, but attracts moisture from the air and passes it down. Anyhow, the effect of this layer of apparently bone-dry cinders, hot to the touch in the burning sunlight, is that, if rain falls only twice in the season, the rich soil produces an excellent harvest—and our informant waved an appreciative hand towards the verdant lentils and maize and vines; potatoes, also, with tubers as round and as large as cherries. When it is desired to plant a fresh crop the cinders are scraped into heaps, the sowing or planting done in the exposed soil, and

the black blanket replaced. The chahorra itself is
the burned-out rock which has been flung into the
air by the volcanoes, for these islands are wholly
volcanic. Only two centuries ago there were
eruptions on a vast scale; mountains of cinders and
seas of lava and of boiling mud were cast forth; and
two thousand centuries ago the same thing was
going on. The present is a period of quiescence,
though only twenty years ago there was a little flare-
up on Tenerife, accompanied by very creditable fireworks. In the south of Lanzarote there is an
agglomeration of eighteenth-century lava streams,
miles in breadth, looking like storm-tossed seas
suddenly frozen; and so hard and glassy is the lava
that its innumerable edges and points are still as
sharp as knives, forming a barrier more impassable
than any ocean. Two hundred years have made
no change in it, and the only relief that nature has
given to the black riven mass is an abundant growth
of grey lichen. But even this is restricted. Look
south and the whole lava-field is green-grey; look
north and all is black and burnt. Where the sunlight strikes in summer the lava becomes so hot that
one cannot touch it even for a moment; only where
it strikes obliquely can even lichens grow.

Where the lava flows are thin, another curiosity
of agriculture may be seen. The Canarios cut down
through the rock to the soil below which formed
the ancient surface, and at the bottom of the holes
thus formed they plant their vines. These root
deeply, and spread their prostrate branches over the
sun-hot rock. Looking across a flow, you do not

see a green leaf, for the holes are cut in the bottoms
of hollows; yet the black expanse may shelter a rich
harvest. Particularly good and abundant fruit is
produced, the yield from a single well-grown plant
being as much as a hundred gallons of wine annu-
ally.

On this island of Lanzarote, the soil is of an amazing fertility, and only the heaven-sent gift of rain
is stinted. To the people no field labour is too
great, and desert cultivation has been reduced to a
fine art. Under their hands the rivers of red-hot
rock that once overwhelmed the land, and the rains
of hot ashes like those which buried Herculaneum
and Pompeii, have alike been turned to human
service; and if the desert does not yet blossom like
the rose, it is at least far removed from its primitive
condition, before human energy attacked the desperate problem of its reclamation.

BEYOND SOUNDINGS.

IT is strange to think how limited is one's knowledge of the sea, which covers the greater part of this world of ours, and forms, for us islanders, a so familiar and significant portion of our environment. What does the landsman know of it? To him it is an extensive more or less muddy liquid, useful for summer ablutions, but capable of causing astonishing perturbation when he is so rash as to venture on its surface. As to its floor, his acquaintance, so far as actual contact is concerned, ceases at a fathom's depth; though on a calm day he may peer from a boat into somewhat deeper water, and note sand and stones, and fishes swimming among the branching seaweeds. And does the sailor know much more of the sea than this? To him, indeed, the surface is familiar in all its aspects of storm and calm, from the Arctic ice, it may be, to the silver-flashing surges of San Salvador. The joyous blue water which replaces, when one gets clear of the land, the dull green sea that surrounds our islands beyond their fringe of muddy river spume, is to him an old story, and the glorious freedom of a thousand miles of ocean surface moving to the music of the trade winds. But what of the middle waters, and of the distant ocean floor? They are as strange to him as to the landsman. Once "beyond soundings" he does not know—nor does he care—whether the sea be one or a hundred miles deep, nor whether its bed be paved with gold or with primeval mud. These things are entirely beyond his ken. And while the life of the surface lies before the eye—seal and nautilus, flying-fish and whale—what terrors may not be hidden in the mysterious miles of depth over which his keel glides so readily? Monk-fish and mermaid, sea-serpent and giant devil-fish: are they all merely the offspring of imagination and fear and sea-sickness? Is it not possible that in the depths there may still persist creatures of types of long ago, which we know only from fossils in the rocks—great armoured fishes perhaps, or the descendants of the terrible ichthyosaurs and plesiosaurs, or the more homely trilobites of an earlier period, so familiar in our older rocks; or may the " green hells of the sea" harbour strange monsters quite unknown to man— perhaps never to be known? Though we may even now say with Empedocles that much may still exist which is not yet believed—especially in so vast and unapproachable a region as the deeper ocean waters —yet a hundred years of steady and laborious research in which every sea-faring nation in the world has taken part, has resulted in a profound insight into the mysteries of life in the ocean. Some long-cherished legends are gone. Mermaid and monk-fish have departed—though indeed plausible specimens of the former, ingeniously compounded of a monkey's head and fish's body, may still be obtained in China by the credulous. There is a tale that Linnæus had once hurriedly to leave some Dutch town for having dared to doubt the genuineness of a specimen of this kind, a treasured household god of some highly placed seeker after truth. Even the sea-serpent, octogenarian of mythical ocean-dwellers, has fallen from his high estate. "Most of the stories of this creature," writes David Starr Jordan in his book on fishes, "are seaman's yarns, sometimes based on a fragment of wreck, a long strip of kelp, the power of suggestion or the incitement of alcohol." But he hastens to add that certain sea-serpent stories relate to real creatures, such as the oarfish, twenty-five feet long, snake-like, with fins projecting above the head like a mane; this creature seen among the waves might readily become a horse-headed monster. But if modern science has robbed us of many picturesque marvels of the deep, it has supplied others still more wonderful, as will be seen later.

Again, what of the Sargasso Sea, out in the western Atlantic, with its dense meadows of floating seaweed stretching over leagues of ocean, in which even great ships become snared, and lie through long months motionless and helpless, while their starving crews watch with horror the grotesque creatures, peculiar to this place of living death, which crawl or swim among the brown branching tangle? Alas, for romance! If one wishes a vivid description of the Sargasso Sea as it is, one may turn to William Beebe's chapter on it in that fascinating book of his, "The Arcturus Adventure." Beebe's ship steamed backwards and forwards across this area from end to end. What of the miles of undulating sea-weed meadow? "We saw numberless patches of weed, but seldom any which were

larger than a man's head. For many days, in storm
and calm, these averaged one to every square hundred yards." What of the weed-clogged vessels?
" The only wrecks were dissolute Welsh colliers
wallowing past on their unpainted way." What of
the crowd of unique creatures inhabiting this unique
floating forest? We are told that the animals which
at certain seasons abound there are not truly
oceanic at all, but come, like the drifting weed itself,
from the coasts of Central America. " It is a terrible
thing to me," adds our author, "to destroy beliefs and
legends." This is all very depressing; but if we go
deeper into the subject of the sea and the creatures
that dwell in it, a romance unfolds that leaves the
mermaids and sea-serpents and rotting hulks forgotten and unwept.

* * * * *

The first and most important problem for all of
us, from man down to his cousin the mosquito, is
where to obtain our breakfast. Not only armies, but
all created things, march on their stomachs. And
all animals require organic substance for food—that
is, those materials which form the bodies of animals
or plants. The animal world cannot *make* organic
food. Neither can all creatures live by eating each
other, any more than we can get rich by taking in
each other's washing. But plants can do what no
animal can. Give them water from the soil or the
sea (containing a trace of dissolved salts) and carbon
dioxide from the air, and they will build up from
these materials their own organic bodies, whether
these be microscopically small or three hundred feet

in height, the energy required for this synthesis being derived from sunlight, through the instrumentality of chlorophyll, which forms the familiar green colouring matter of plants. On the existence and continuance of this activity in the vegetable world the life of the whole animal kingdom depends absolutely. On land the incidence of this law is familiar in a hundred forms. Save where it is too cold or too dry, the continents are covered with vegetation. One half the animal kingdom, from green-flies to elephants, obtain their nourishment directly from this plant-mantle; the other half, from tomtits to tigers, prey on the vegetable feeders directly or indirectly. With plant-food so abundant, the prosperity of the animal world on land appears assured. But what about the sea? The sea contains a vast population, beside which that of the land sinks into insignificance; but where is the food supply for these countless hordes? Seaweeds in abundance there are, clothing the rocks between tides, and extending downwards to a certain depth: but this depth is negligible. Seaweeds like land plants must have light; and light becomes very dim under a few fathoms of water. In consequence the seaweeds that we know form the merest narrow fringe round the edge of the land, whereas the ocean is populous with creatures from shore to shore, and from the surface down to miles of depth. The microscope reveals the clue to this mystery. Every drop of sea water taken at or near the surface is found to be crowded with very minute plants, known as diatoms. In countless millions they swarm and propagate, from the pole to the equator, absorbing solar energy and using it to build up the complicated chemical substances which form their bodies. Countless millions of minute animals find in these microscopic plants their food supply, breaking down in the course of digestion the materials of the plant-body, and utilising for the purposes of their own lives the energy thus set free. On these microscopic animal forms, in turn, larger sea-beasts prey, and so on, it may be through a chain of many links, till we reach the giants of the ocean. On land the similar chain of food-supply is interwoven across the surface only, or very close to it. In the sea it originates on the surface, but is by no means confined thereto; its links spread downward into the profoundest depths, sometimes in the form of living animals, often as dead matter, sinking slowly to provide nourishment for the hungry creatures of the middle waters and of the distant ocean floor. So it comes about that the life of the depths owes its existence and continuance wholly to that sun which, for the creatures living under that black pall of water, might be deemed as ineffective as the furthest star.

The abundance of this minute life of the ocean, not only in the surface waters but far down into the depths, staggers the imagination. A single cupful of water may contain, according to place and season, tens of thousands or hundreds of thousands of minute plants and animals. No less astonishing is their power of propagation, against which one may set their wholesale destruction at the hands of the creatures that prey upon them. An ordinary marine bacterium will, in the course of a week or two under normal circumstances, multiply to the extent of several millions. On the other side we find that the stomach of a single sardine has been estimated to contain twenty millions of Ceratium, one of the commoner infusoria, to whose presence phosphorescence in the sea is frequently due. The author the " Water Babies," in writing of the old whale's mouthful of " 943 seamoths, 13,846 jelly-fish no bigger than pins' heads, a string of salpa nine yards long, and forty-three little ice-crabs," far from exaggerating, mentioned only a tithe of the creatures that would be enveloped in one gulp in "that terrible whalebone net of his." But large figures convey a poor idea of actual numbers; when they pass beyond thousands, it matters little whether they be millions or billions; the mind cannot envisage them. Suffice it to say that life in the sea, especially, but not only, among the smaller organisms, its profusion, its fecundity, and the destruction to which it is subject, is on a scale which beggars imagination, and puts in the shade completely those terrestrial irruptions or holocausts—of voles, lemmings, locusts, or what not—of which one occasionally reads with wonderment. The scale on which both production and destruction proceed in the drama of ocean life is well symbolised in Kipling's fable (in " The Butterfly that Stamped"), when the Animal which ate in three mouthfuls the food which Solomon had prepared for all the beasts in all the world says: "I am the smallest of thirty thousand brothers, and our home is at the bottom of the sea. We heard that you were going to feed all the animals in all the world, and my brothers sent me to ask when dinner would be ready." Solomon: " O Animal, you have eaten all the dinner that I made ready for all the animals in the world." The Animal: " O King, live for ever, but do you really call *that* a dinner? Where I come from we eat twice as much as that between meals."

But there are other conditions besides that of food supply controlling life in the abyss—conditions which it is hard for us dwellers of the wind and sunshine to realise. All round the coasts the sea-bottom slopes fairly rapidly till a depth of two to four miles is reached, when vast slightly undulating plains spread for thousands of miles. Below a hundred fathoms or two not only has all wave action ceased, but perceptible currents are absent; absolute stillness prevails, allowing the accumulation of fine mud stretching unbroken across these submarine continents. Light ceases to penetrate beyond a depth insignificant in comparison with that of the ocean, and in the deeper waters utter darkness reigns. With no sun to warm it, and slow icy currents creeping down from the poles, the temperature of the depths remains always near freezing point. And everywhere is the tremendous pressure due to miles of superincumbent water. On the floor of the Atlantic this averages about $2\frac{1}{2}$ tons on every square inch: in the deepest waters known it is as much as 6 tons—nearly 8,000 tons to the square yard. Not that this extraordinary weight is necessarily deleterious to life. It is only the unequal distribution of pressure that causes catastrophe, from a headache to a volcanic eruption. The deep-sea creatures, subject from their very birth to this pressure through every organ and every blood-corpuscle, suffer no detriment from it: just as we ourselves support unconsciously a weight of nearly a ton on every square foot of our bodies, due to the atmosphere, and are inconvenienced only when we diminish or increase that pressure by climbing a high mountain or descending into the compressed air caisson of some deep foundation. These, then, are the conditions under which life in the ocean abysses exists —utter darkness, low temperature, stupendous pressure, absolute stillness. The only movement, apart from that of living creatures, is the imperceptible slow raining down of débris from the surface and superincumbent waters—mainly the limy or flinty skeletons of animals, large or small, and meteoric dust. In the deepest parts of the ocean, the calcareous and even the siliceous matter is dissolved before it ever reaches the floor; and metallic red clay, largely the wreck of meteors, covers wide areas. As depth decreases, first siliceous skeletons (especially of Radiolaria) and then calcareous skeletons (particularly of Foraminifera) are deposited and form in the course of ages deep beds of mud.

And what of the creatures which live under the strange conditions outlined above? It is a surprise to find that life in the depths is abundant and varied. The middle and lower waters are the home of a great variety of roaming fishes, cuttle-fishes, and smaller organisms, while on the ocean floor all kinds of creatures maintain a more sedentary existence

—molluscs, crabs, prawns, star-fishes, sea-urchins, worms, sponges, and what not. The fishes of the abyss are of all sizes and shapes, from gigantic sharks to mere sprats; they are mostly of a dull or black colour, without the spots or stripes which decorate many of their fellows in the lighted waters above and often act so efficiently as camouflage. But many of the invertebrates of the depths, such as the prawns and star-fishes, are most brilliantly coloured, orange and scarlet and imperial purple. The eyes of the deep-sea creatures are mostly very large, or altogether wanting—as if they were either optimists still hoping to see in those inky waters, or pessimists, which had long since given up the attempt. But there is a reason for eyes in the abyss, and this introduces one of the most remarkable features of the deep-sea fauna. Deprived of the light of the sun, most of the animals have developed illuminating systems of their own. Creatures of many kinds —fishes, crustacea, star-fishes, worms, etc.—emit phosphorescent light, which flashes or glows. This may be confined to certain parts or distributed over the whole body. Some fishes have rows of brightly shining spots along their sides which make them look like miniature ocean liners. Others have brilliant searchlights; others again glimmer all over with a ghostly pale glow. Some of the prawns can emit a luminous cloud—a glowing smoke screen behind which they can retreat before an enemy, just as some of the squids emit a cloud of ink. " The squid has its column of smoke by day, the prawn its pillar of fire by night." This lighting-up in its various forms may serve to attract or to repel—a signal to friends, or a warning to foes. Sometimes it is used as a lure. Let us consider briefly one of the most remarkable groups of deep-sea fishes, the anglers or sea-devils, which illustrate this last point, as well as the strange forms, the voracity and the peculiar adaptation to surroundings which are all so remarkably developed among abysmal creatures. One of these anglers is a familiar fish of our own shallow waters—an ugly flattened brute with a huge mouth filled with wicked teeth, and a strange fishing-rod decked with a tassel, projecting beyond the head, and used as a bait to attract unwary creatures. This Fishing Frog is as strange and hideous a creature as one can imagine, and its outrageous appetite is shown by the fact that one was found to have made a dinner of seven wild ducks! But it is surpassed by its deep-water relations. Imagine a fish black all over, almost all head, and the head almost all mouth, so that the mouth occupies three-quarters of the whole creature; of strange angular outline, short and deep; and projecting forwards from behind the head a regular fishing-rod, jointed at the tip and continued as a fine fishing-line with a little shining lamp at the end, which dangles in front of those terrible rows of teeth to lure other fishes to their doom. Rod and line may be four times the length of the fish itself. Conceive this jet-black sea-devil hovering motionless in the jet-black water, its huge jaws open, its waving lantern lure alone visible. Woe to the fish which is attracted by that will-o'-the wisp; for those huge jaws have stomach to match, stomach extensible beyond belief, so that these creatures can not only capture and kill, but swallow and ultimately digest fishes which may be four or five times their own length. For hideousness, voracity, and ingenuity combined these sea-devils are hard to match. But this does not exhaust the tale of their strangeness. Several specimens from different parts of the ocean were found to have small similar fishes attached to them —to the head or to the under side of the body— which were at first taken to be their young. But the character of these, combined with the fact that the fishes with which they were associated were found to be invariably females, has led to the discovery that they are males, degenerate in structure and permanently parasitic upon the females. The life-history of the males appears to be as follows: they begin life as ordinary free-swimming young, but quite early they attach themselves by their jaws to a female—possibly to the first one which they meet. Their lips grow out and fuse with the flesh of the female, so that eventually it becomes impossible to say where one fish ends and the other begins. While the females continue to grow, in some cases to a considerable size, the males remain quite small —only a hundredth or it may be a thousandth of the bulk of the others. They become utterly degenerate. The mouth closes, the alimentary system becomes obsolete and useless. The blood system of the two becomes continuous, and the male practically an appendage of the female, living while she lives, and dying when she dies. It is a story unparalleled among the vertebrate animals, finding a sort of analogy only among a few very lowly creatures; a story which zoologists could not have accepted as possible, were it not that actual specimens, fully studied, have shown its truth.

Plenty of other wonder-tales of the ocean there are also. What of the sperm-whales which attack and eat giant cuttle-fishes, up to 50 feet long, in the middle waters of the deep sea? For long the origin of certain curious indented marks on the heads and bodies of these whales was a mystery; but the finding by the Prince of Monaco and other ocean fishermen of remains of new and strange cuttle-fishes in the whales' stomachs gave a clue. They were the marks of the formidable suckers of the devil-fishes; creatures as terrific as the classic one in the "Toilers of the Sea." What titanic battles must those be between the greatest of the mammals and the greatest of the molluscs!

And what of the marvellous tale of the eels, which as tiny transparent ribbons disperse slowly from their great single breeding-ground two-thirds way across the Atlantic, off the Gulf of Mexico? They reach at length, after several years of wandering, the coasts of North America or western Europe or the Mediterranean. They ascend the rivers, and live in them quietly for years till they attain maturity. Then one autumn the skin becomes more silvery, the eyes larger; a mysterious influence causes them to forsake their river haunts and commence a journey of it may be four thousand miles across the ocean back to their birthplace, from which they are destined never to return. Here, in the abysses of the Atlantic they assemble—the eels of all the world, from Thames and Tiber, Neva and Nile, St. Lawrence and Mississippi; and here they breed, to give rise to millions of tiny transparent flattened young, which in turn work their way slowly across the surface of the ocean and ascend the rivers to become the familiar slippery creatures which we find in every brook. Stranger still, though all start together to seek their fortunes, the young American eels never come to Europe, nor the European eels to America. How is it done?

GINKGO AND TUMBOA.

THERE is something in a name after all. If this discourse were headed " Buttercups and Daisies " or " Lettuces and Leeks," the reader's eye might pass it lightly by; but who could fail to be " intrigued " (I believe that is still the correct word) by "Ginkgo and Tumboa"? Why, it might connote anything, from the label of the latest cure-me-quick to the *nom-de-guerre* of a tandem of music hall stars of the first magnitude. As it is, it stands for two of the most strange and interesting plants upon this earth—the one a beautiful and stately tree, sacred besides, and associated with ancient temple-gardens in China and Japan; the other a nightmare monstrosity, like a gigantic sea-anemone gone mad, squatting on lonely rainless deserts in south-western Africa. But the peculiar interest of both lies not merely in their appearance. Each is a relic of a bygone kingdom, a lonely representative—in the case of Ginkgo the only one now left in the world—of a race once powerful and numerous. It is as if a pterodactyl, bat-winged, dragon-headed, still hurtled through our skies; as if the Brontosaurus, lately the subject of a newspaper myth, yet lived in very truth.

To place these plants in a proper perspective, it is necessary to glance historically at the past life of the globe. This is a story that does not make easy reading even to those who know the language, for all the earlier chapters are lost, and none of those that remain are anything like complete—many of them quite fragmentary. The fossil record gives mere glimpses of the ancient vegetations. The oldest rocks which contain plant remains sufficiently well preserved for study are already high up in the sequence of the sedimentary succession, and the plants which they yield are highly organized, and have evidently a very long history behind them. Yet even these rocks were laid down at a time immensely remote. It is almost impossible (though often attempted) to express geological age according to human time-standards, but perhaps if we set down the date of this oldest well-preserved flora, from the rocks that geologists call Devonian, as forty or fifty millions of years ago, we should not be wrong by more than a hundred per cent. This Devonian vegetation was apparently as abundant and nearly as varied as the vegetation of to-day. Most of the great groups of the plant world, which at one time or another have played a leading part, were present—seaweeds, horsetails, ferns, club-mosses, and a higher but long extinct group, the pteridosperms, which looked like ferns, but were really more nearly allied to the Flowering Plants. But we miss entirely the angiosperms, or true Flowering Plants, which dominate the world to-day, in all situations—hot and cold, wet and dry—save only the salt waters of the earth, where the sea-weeds still maintain their ancient solitary reign. The animal world in those Devonian times was even more different from that of nowadays, for scarcely a creature existed recalling the characteristic forms of our time. The seas and lakes were full of fishes it is true, of strange appearance, but there was nothing even distantly resembling our familiar animals—elephants or mice, horses or wolves, kangaroos or whales; and the sky was as lonely as the land, for no birds were flying overhead—there were no birds to fly! Yet even in those distant times it would appear that a close ally of our Ginkgo or Maidenhair Tree was already in existence, if a correct interpretation has been placed on a certain fossil plant found in Devonian sandstone at Kiltorcan in County Kilkenny. But the affinities of many of the plants from rocks even much less ancient than the Devonian are still obscure, for the fossils which alone tell us of the life of those times are fragmentary, and often badly preserved. It is only when we come to the Jurassic period, many millions of years later, that the group to which the Maidenhair Tree belongs stands out indubitably in the rocks, and attains a considerable importance and variety of form over a wide area of the earth's surface. In American rocks of the same period appear the earliest fossils which are believed to be the forerunners of our other strange plant, Tumboa. It is interesting to try to picture the ancient Jurassic world in which these types existed. In those days the rain fell and the wind blew as they do at present, but the distribution of heat was such that a subtropical vegetation flourished in Spitsbergen. All the familiar Flowering Plants which now form our woodlands and grasslands, and haunt mountain and valley, were still unknown.

The forests were composed of the ancient group of horsetails, of conifers of primitive type, of Ginkgo and its cousins; notably of screw-pines or cycads, an early group which still exists in diminished numbers; and under their shade numerous ferns and lower plants abounded. Insects of strange shape and of many kinds flitted through the glades. The absence of all our familiar types of birds and mammals was still complete. But their place was taken by reptiles of such an amazing variety of form and size as to cause this period to be called the "Age of Reptiles." In the sea there were great crocodile-like beasts, long slender creatures like finned serpents, and other other fantastic forms somewhat resembling huge leather-coated swans. The air was full of flying monsters large and small, bat-like or bird-like, with strong teeth in their powerful jaws; veritable dragons. But it was on land that the reptilian population took on its most fantastic appearance. Creatures of grotesque and terrifying aspect roamed over the land, or haunted the rivers and forests, browsing on the trees or devouring each other. Some were no larger than a hen; at the other end of the scale were monsters like Diplodacus and Atlantosaurus, measuring up to 80 feet from head to tail, and weighing over 20 tons. Recently comes the news of the discovery of the remains of a monster twice as large as these, which has been named Gigantosaurus. Towards the close of Jurassic times there appear at length the direct forerunners of the birds and mammals which are so important in the life of to-day. The oldest known bird was about the size of a crow, and if it was two-thirds bird it was one-third reptile, having evidently evolved from a reptilian stock. The earliest mammals had affinities with the lowest orders of mammals which now inhabit the earth, the marsupials (kangaroos, opossums, etc.), and the monotremes (Platypus and so on). During the earlier part of the period which succeeded, known as the Cretaceous (to which the white chalk of England and Antrim belongs) the general character of the flora did not change much, but in the later rocks of this time are found many of the forerunners of our present vegetation. Among the animals, huge reptiles were still conspicuous, and weird birds with strong teeth held dominion in the air. The following Eocene period witnessed the extinction of the great reptiles, and their place was taken by the ancestors of most of our modern beasts and birds, and also of man; similarly among the plants, we find in the Eocene rocks the direct forerunners of our modern vegetation, with a greatly reduced proportion of the older races, including the Ginkgoaceæ and Gnetales.

Further than this we need not trace the pedigree or history of the plants of our text. They diminished in numbers as the great modern race of Flowering Plants sprang more and more into dominance; till to-day we find Ginkgo the sole representative of its ancient and once powerful family, while Tumboa is the most remarkable of three small groups which alone now represent the whole class of Gnetales.

A few words as to the appearance of these two

relics of bygone ages. Ginkgo, now unknown in a
wild state but preserved to us in the Far East by
reason of its being a sacred tree, is tall and graceful,
and attains a height of 100 feet. It gets its English
name from the peculiar and characteristic shape
of its leaves, which resemble the pinnules of a
maidenhair fern—fan-shaped, with forked veins of
a primitive type. Its botanical name is imported
from Japan. The fruit is like a small plum, with a
" stone " in the middle, and golden flesh with a
singularly unpleasant smell. Ginkgo grows well in
our climate, and is to be seen in most collections
of trees. Tumboa, on the other hand, though forming a massive kind of trunk, rises barely above the
ground. Conceive an irregular two-lobed roundish
mass, flattish on top, a yard or two across, woody,
covered with old cracked bark. Arising from the
margin, an opposite pair of great strap-shaped leaves
a couple of yards long, which never die, but keep
on growing from the plant's birth till its death, a
period of a hundred years or more; these leaves
sprawl and curl along the ground, their extremities
cut into ribbons by wind and weather, and slowly
decaying as the leaf lengthens. And just inside the
leaves, still close to the rim, branching panicles of
scarlet cones, like those of a spruce. This is the
queer plant which confronted Frederic Welwitsch,
the well-known explorer, in stony deserts near Cape
Negro in 1860—one of the most sensational dis-
coveries which it ever fell to the lot of the botanist
to make. Sir Joseph Hooker proposed to name it
Welwitschia after its finder, but Dr. Welwitsch had

already quoted for it the native name of Tumboa, which according to botanical law takes precedence. It is seldom to be seen in botanic gardens, as it has proved very difficult to cultivate.

ISLAND FOLK.

" See Rachray Island beyont in the bay,
    An' the dear knows what they be doin' out there
But fishin' an' fightin' an' tearin' away,
    An' who's to hindher, an' what do they care?"

THIS lively picture no doubt represents one aspect
of island life, but in general, society on these
sea-girt spots appeals rather by its placidity, its
patriarchal simplicity, and its note of mutual
tolerance and helpfulness. The absence of trains
and hooters, picture-houses and policemen, makes
towards a quiet and deliberate life; the stress of
island conditions tends to bind the people together;
co-operation in enterprises which they consider to
be for the common advantage may take forms
looked on with disfavour by the law, like the making of poteen; but on the other hand, the common
individualistic trespassings of the town, such as
confusion of thought regarding *mine* and *thine,* are
almost unknown. To be overcome by liquor now
and again is an accident that may happen to any
man; a casual fight leaves no bad blood behind; and
if occasionally a transgression calls for punishment,
that follows in due course, and is accepted philosophically. Is it not told how in Aran in years still
recent, when The O'Flaherty, sole arbiter of law,
passed sentence and awarded a month of seclusion,
the delinquent would take boat across to Conne-

mara, tramp to Galway, and deliver his message
and himself to the governor of the gaol; and when
his time was up, tramp back to Cashla and wait for
a turf-boat to take him home again.

On the islands, time acquires a new interpretation; sunrise and moonrise are more important than
this or that hour of the clock; the varying incidence
of high tide and the capricious wind leads to lonely
vigils, and to comings and goings at all hours of day
and night; and the people gain a knowledge of both
land and sea under all conditions such as town
dwellers can scarcely realise. From your cottage
window at the first peep of dawn, in summer or in
winter, you may see your boatmen perched together
smoking and chatting, quite oblivious of the drench-
ing rain, but keeping a sharp eye on the chances of
wind and sea; and they can tell you all that has
passed during the night.

It is interesting to think of our Irish islands as
they were a thousand years ago—before the Con-
gested Districts Board had " striped " the land and
generally tidied things up, before the fretwork of
fences and stone walls had come into being, before
the people had changed the naked limestone ledges
of Aran into pasture and tillage by carrying on their
backs sand and seaweed from the shore. Then one
might have wandered unchecked across the flower-
decked rocks to a more complete and imposing Dun
Aengus, with only the birds for company, while
over by Killeany the low buildings of the ecclesiastics rose against the sky.

To the north-west of Aran, against the Connemara

shore, where Inishmacdara lies, a mere whale-
backed reef of granite supporting a few acres of
coarse grass, the anchorite had his cell. On the
windward side of the islet, the Atlantic waves have
swept the rock bare and smooth for a breadth of a
quarter of a mile, and on the upper limit of this
storm-beach they have piled a rampart of blocks
each weighing many tons. Yet on this desolate spot,
where the waves thunder as of old, we may still see
a trace of the hermit's attempt at a kitchen garden,
for hard by the tiny ruined church the Elecampane
grows yet, a plant first brought from Central Europe
by the monks, who had a high opinion of its medicinal value—" Enula campana reddit præcordia
sana."

And think of those desperate hermits on the Great
Skellig, a rock like a church steeple, in their huts
plastered against the cliff face like swallows' nests,
with the Atlantic rollers raving for ever below, and
miles of angry water between them and any in-
habited land, forbidding for months at a time all
communication with their fellows. Surely no
romance ever pictured a life so savage and austere.

Indeed, in romantic literature, whether drama,
poetry, or prose, the people who are associated with
an island existence seem to take the view that while
islands may or may not be attractive as temporary
residences, they are on the whole very good places
to live out of; and this in spite of the opportunities
which they offer for unlimited bathing, and the
absence of income tax, fashion papers, and snakes.
Calypso and Crusoe, Ellen Douglas and poor Ben

Gunn, all give at best a qualified praise to island life, and seem to have been frankly glad to return to a more cosmopolitan existence. It may be that, at least to those who have not had the advantages of an insular upbringing, islands are most beneficial when taken in homœopathic doses.

I should love to wander through all the little islands of the world. Perhaps in some reincarnation that will be permitted, but in this life time is short, and ocean travel needs many pennies. Only a very few islands has it been my fortune to visit— St. Kilda, where we wandered with the Kearton brothers in fog and pouring rain along the ledges of gigantic cliffs among the nesting gannets, searching for the gannet's tiny and elusive cousin, the St. Kilda wren; the little flat islets of the East Frisian group, like rafts on the shallow sea, each with an absurdly large barn-like farmhouse upon it, sticking up like the bridge of a hull-down steamer, peopled by pleasant simple folk still wearing quaint medieval costume, and speaking a tongue that is very close to English. The Lofoten Islands offered a wide contrast to these, bare rock towering thousands of feet up into the cold clear air, flecked with green mosses and other plants below, wherever great colonies of sea-birds had not taken possession; while high up against the sky little hanging glaciers gleamed in the midnight sunlight, threatening to fall bodily into the fathomless water of dusky inlets visited only by the innumerable boats of the fisher-folk.

In contrast to these again, the fairy sunlit islands of the Canary and Madeira groups. To a large num-

ber of people, I fancy, Madeira spells Reid's Palace
Hotel; Gran Canaria recalls that atrocious road, all
dust, ruts, lean mules and hideous buildings, that
trails its stifling length from Puerto de la Luz to
Las Palmas; and Tenerife brings up chiefly visions
of the narrow streets and gimcrack shops of Santa
Cruz. For on these islands roads are few and hotels
are fewer, and unless one is willing to forsake English standards for a while one's orbit is limited;
through all their loveliest parts—and how lovely
they are—only rough mule tracks lead, zigzagging
over breakneck mountains and through cliff-walled
gorges. The towns breed a motley crowd; but when
they are left behind one is among a delightful island
race—simple, hospitable, athletic, and charming in
face, figure, and dress. The men and boys—and the
girls too—walk the gigantic precipices like goats,
tilling their tiny patches of tomatoes and vines
perched, it may be, a couple of thousand feet above
their homes. The women tend the stock, or sit in
the shade over their embroidery frames; to see
them walk is a delight, for they have the lovely
poise that comes from bearing loads on the head.
To watch a string of brightly-dressed young girls
tripping laughingly up a ladder-like track, each with
a 40 lb. can of water balanced on a little coiled ker-
chief on her shapely head, is something to be
remembered.

And these Canarios retain a courtliness worthy of
their Spanish ancestry. I recall a wide desolate
mountain-valley, full of queer cactus-like spurge—of
a species, by the way, found nowhere else in the

world—and narrowing at the head to a wall-like pass; among the rocks one lonely cottage; and waiting for us, as our camels shuffle up the steep track, an old man and woman. He has caught and milked a goat, while she has plundered of its few blossoms her two square yards of garden; and they wait to offer a greeting to the strangers, and to press on them their simple hospitality.

Or again, a steep narrow street in Valverde, perched on the stony hillside of Hierro, high above the ocean. Old people sitting in the doorways; children playing in the dusty sunlight; a group of Spanish infantrymen and black-eyed girls. An old dame calls after us—her daughter begs permission to offer a flower to the donna Inglese. A little crowd gathers by magic: the soldiers stand at attention: a young woman with a face like a Madonna, a child on her arm, comes forward shyly and fastens a rose on my wife's bosom. There is a murmur of approval and goodwill: the soldiers salute. We stand abashed, taken by surprise, and hampered by a very sketchy acquaintance with Spanish: then stammer thanks as best we can, and pass on amid friendly adieux.

CABBAGES AND KINGS.

THE Walrus, whose version of "Come unto these Yellow Sands" had such tragic consequences for the too confiding molluscs, was an epicure and a profound philosopher. It is true that he chose for companion a materialist and a sceptic unworthy of the honour of his society, but possibly the conjunction of the two was fortuitous. On the other hand, not only did he show an unerring instinct in the way of *hors d'œuvres* (which seemingly, as in Norwegian hotels, was a meal in itself) but in his benign if irrelevant observations addressed to the oysters he sums up in a lightning flash, in a single masterly sentence, the whole biological history of the earth. His boiling sea evokes a vision of that remote time preceding the earliest stirrings of organic nature when, during the ages following on the solidification of the terrestrial crust, the vast envelope of water vapour which shrouded it became condensed upon its surface, preparing the way for the first dim dawn of Life. The question as to flying swine brings us down some millions of years later to that fascinating period when the great Reptile empire which in Liassic times dominated alike the land and the waters and the air crumbled away, to give rise phœnix-like to the more noble kingdoms of Quadrupeds and Birds—the one adapted for running, the other for flight; the former undisputed lords of the earth prior to the appearance of man, the latter still the masters of the air, despite the efforts of our unstable roaring aeroplanes. As to shoes and ships and sealing-wax, the allusion is obvious; it refers to one of the most remarkable of man's achievements, far-reaching, yet still in its infancy—the development of human communications, by land and sea, by the written as well as the spoken word. Thus in three lines does our seer vouchsafe to us instantaneous glimpses into as many momentous periods in the long-drawn history of our Earth and its multitudinous inhabitants.

But of still greater significance is his reference to Cabbages and Kings, and particularly the close juxtaposition in which he places them, for here is indicated in a nutshell the present state of biological evolution upon our vicissitudinous planet—namely, the overwhelming dominance of the Angiosperms or Flowering Plants upon the one hand, and of that restless and revolutionary creature *Homo sapiens* upon the other, and the close and intimate association of the two. It is particularly noteworthy that Cabbages, as representing the highest families in the vegetable world, are awarded priority to Kings, which here typify the human race, highest of the animal creation; for that is their proper sequence, whether regarded from an evolutionary or an economic standpoint. This weighty phrase, with its profound implications, which the Walrus wasted on the oysters (since he subsequently devoured them) is worthy of our serious consideration, and if I may venture to attempt to expound the meaning of so profound a mystic, here goes. But the subject is so vast, embracing the whole history of creation upon the Earth, from its obscure beginnings, through manifold revolutions and actions and reactions, down to the intricate life-manifestations of the present time, that all the books in the world would not suffice for its exposition; only an occasional pin-point of suggestion can be seized upon and to some slight degree elaborated.

First as to the hot seas and the origin of life. Active living matter, as we know it on this Earth, is strictly controlled by conditions of temperature. It cannot function at higher than about half-way between the freezing point and the boiling point of water. There is no reason to believe that the more primitive and ancient forms of life differed in this respect from those which we can still study. The assumption is justified, therefore, that life did not begin till what was relatively a quite low temperature had been reached upon the Earth's surface. We have to envisage an immense period of time during which the Earth cooled from an incandescent state down to a condition which, in the range of temperatures which exists in the universe, is actually very cold. And then, or at some indefinite subsequent period, a strange thing happened. Certain compounds of carbon, hydrogen, ogygen and nitrogen, mixed with small quantities of mineral salts, acquired the astonishing power not only of increasing their bulk by the absorption and transformation of similar materials, but of division into units of uniform size and shape, and of increase in the number of such units by a process of splitting. Other remarkable attributes followed. The units developed for their protection an outer covering or cell-wall, cells acquired the power of motion by the lashing of whip-like threads or ciliæ, and through an ascending scale of size (by the agglomeration of masses of cells), of intricacy of structure and so forth, organic life advanced. Where did the energy come from to enable this work to be carried out? It came from the sun: sunlight supplied, as it still does for the whole vegetable and animal worlds, the ultimate source of all the energy required for all life and growth. This is accomplished, and has been accomplished, possibly from the very dawn of life, through the medium of chlorophyll, that substance which makes plants appear green to our eyes. In the presence of sunlight, chlorophyll performs the miracle of turning dead into living matter.

That this mysterious thing we call Life began in the water, not on the land, there can be little doubt. Even to-day all plants and animals consist principally of water, and are absolutely dependent on its supply for their continued existence. Very significant is the fact that in no animals, and only in the highest and most recently evolved races of plants, can that most important episode in the organism's whole existence—the fertilization of the egg-cell—be accomplished save through the direct medium of water. We may with some confidence assume the existence of a vast and varied sea population, while the primitive land was still untenanted. The discovery and invasion of the land, with its invigorating sunshine and oxygen-laden wind, was an event of immense import in the history of life on the Globe; it allowed of development and expansion such as might never have taken place in the water. To-day, as for a long period of the past, all the highest forms of animals and plants are terrestrial, not aquatic.

But we must return to very early times to consider that most curious of all the developments which followed the beginnings of life upon the Earth: the segregation of living things into two great groups —plants and animals. That these had a common origin appears certain, for even at the present time there is no marked division between animal and plant towards the bottom of the ladder of life. Indeed, well up in the scale of organization stands out a world-wide group, the Mycetozoa or slime-fungi, which to all intents and purposes are plants for half their life and animals for the other half, so that both zoologists and botanists claim them as belonging to their sphere of study. But usually, and in all higher forms, plants and animals are well differentiated, and the interesting question arises, which, if either, was the earlier—the older and original form of life? Or did they arise simultaneously? On this point a definite answer is possible. Animals, though they are built up mainly of the same materials as vegetables, lack that marvellous substance chlorophyll, by means of which plants compose their living bodies out of water and carbon dioxide and mineral matter. All that animals can do is to utilise the organic substances which plants have produced. They may use these materials directly, as do grazing beasts, or indirectly, by preying upon other animals; but their prey, or the prey of their prey, is ultimately dependent on plants for its subsistence. Thus the whole animal world is a secondary life-manifestation, relying entirely for its continuance on that primary source of all life, the green plant; as parasitic, in fact, as the larva of a Cabbage Butterfly upon a cabbage. Nor is proud man any exception; directly or indirectly, sunlight beating upon green leaves is the source of all our physical being. This is where the Cabbage has the laugh over the King.

Not but that there are certain essential reciprocal activities. The two great groups of organisms have not co-existed upon the Earth for millions of years without the evolution of many intricate inter-relationships. The careless insects, flitting for food from flower to flower, and incidentally pollinating them and thus ensuring the production of seed, are more important for the safety of the human race than all the plans of all the politicians, than all the Acts of all the Parliaments. It might tend to make us a little more humble to reflect that we are mere pensioners of the grasses of the field, that we hold our lives at the whim of a butterfly. Not only that, but we are equally or still more dependent for our continued existence upon even the minutest and most lowly of all known forms of life, such as the invisible bacteria, which in many different ways render this world habitable for us. A single instance must suffice. Plants are built up largely of carbon, which they extract from the carbon dioxide present in the atmosphere. When plants die, the decay of their bodies is due entirely to bacteria. By this process the materials return to the soil and to the air, to be used again by fresh generations. Decay, which we associate with death, is really a manifestation of life—of the living and feeding of millions of bacteria, with consequent chemical changes. In their absence, all decay of organic material would be arrested. The bodies of thousands of generations of plants and animals, still lying where they died and as they died, would lock up within them all the carbon dioxide in the air; vegetable life would in consequence cease, and with it all animal existence would pass away, and the sun would shine, not upon a " habitable flowery earth-rind," but upon a vast charnel-house.

Through endless action and interaction between animals and plants and their physical environment does this complicated life-machine go on; through millions of past years, and apparently for millions of years to come. The fresh knowledge that science continually acquires as to its present-day manifestations serves but to open in all directions new vistas of the mysterious, the unexplored, and the unknown. Will we ever understand its meaning, realise its infinite complexity, learn fully its past history, envisage even dimly whither it is tending? The Walrus's uncommunicative companion supplies the appropriate answer—" I doubt it," said the Carpenter.

PLANTS I HAVE KILLED.

WAS it Frederick the Great who used to greet a new physician with the enquiry," Well, how many grave-yards have *you* filled?" Were the same gibe addressed to me, I could, like many another rock gardener, only bow my head. For, indeed, unless one is satisfied to lie ignobly at anchor in the safe haven of London Pride and Periwinkle, casualties are frequent on board, and one's course is punctuated with burial services. A dim perspective of beloved ghosts stretches behind one, ever lengthening as the years roll on. I am not referring now to such notorious fade-aways as *Hudsonia ericoides* or *Eritrichium nanum* or *Saxifraga florulenta* or *Schizocodon soldanelloides*. There is no credit in killing them—any fool can do that. If one has any enterprise at all, the list of things that one has loved and lost is a long one: it gives rise to many conflicting thoughts; and a little meditation upon it is a salutary exercise, and conducive to humbleness of mind.

As in most problems of gardening, it is difficult to generalise on this matter, because one's failures are in a considerable measure dependent on the conditions of soil and climate under which one works. So as regards personal reminiscences in the remarks which follow, it is necessary to premise that my domain consisted of a small suburban Dublin garden, with a mild climate (though not very mild for Ireland) and a light loamy limy soil. The limitations of such a garden are obvious. Save in pockets of peat, no Ericaceæ will survive, except for the few precious things, like *Rhododendron hirsutum* and *Erica carnea*, which do not care where they grow. No damp-loving plants either, like *Ourisia coccinea* and many species of Mimulus. But indeed, as regards plants of wet places, I have been more surprised at the things that have contrived to live than at those which gave up the attempt. The marsh fern, *Lastrea Thelypteris*, appeared in some mysterious way in a clump of *Anthyllis montana*—the one a plant of soaking swamps, often under water for half the year, the other from the hot rocks of southern Europe; and they still live amicably together. The graceful *Carex Pseudo-cyperus*, another " wet " plant, wandered about the garden (by seed) looking for a spot moist enough to settle down in, and never finding one.

Every gardener has, of course, his list of plants which he longs to grow, but which are just too tender for the particular climate with which he is afflicted. We in Ireland are, in general, well off in this respect as compared with our English and Scottish neighbours; but, just as no one has quite as much money as he considers he ought to have, so everyone's climate is just a degree or two too cold. Among the plants which will grow here for a few years, only to be destroyed just when they are beginning to look really happy, are *Dendromecon rigidum*, *Sollya heterophylla* with its pretty blue flowers, *Billardiera longiflora* with its blue berries,

Cineraria lobata—a gay little thing never out of flower—*Senecio leucostachys*, and many others. Their decease is always the more regretted since all are quite hardy only a few miles away, down by the sea. But, after all, there is no reason to repine: it is our first duty to learn our climatic limitations and to accept them; there's lots of good fish in the sea, and we need not don mourning.

More annoying in reality are those plants which will grow with you if they choose, and won't if they don't. That is all there is to it. There is no use in coaxing them or coddling them, or providing them with complicated composts or ideal nooks. If they won't, they won't, even though they may flourish like weeds in a neighbour's garden. The plants which come under this woeful category no doubt vary in different parts of the country. Visions of *Iris reticulata* arise in my mind in this connection, to quote only one example; and I think many people would add *Gentiana acaulis* (so-called).

Then there are the curious instancse of plants which will grow in one's garden where *they* choose, but not where *you* choose. With me, *Iris hispanica* rapidly died out everywhere it was planted, but sowed itself between two blocks of stone, and, tightly wedged in, it increases year by year. *Galanthus Elwesii* behaved similarly, choosing its own apparently very unsuitable home.

Much more distressing than these are the plants which are equally unwilling to live or to die. An excellent—or rather, horrible—example of this with me is the citrange, a hybrid citrus sent out for

experimental purposes some years ago by the United
States Department of Agriculture. I never look at
it without thinking of Calverley's parakeet:

> He'd look inimitable stuff'd
> And knows it—but he will not die!

Every spring it pretends to start growth, and then
changes its mind. Like Wordsworth's thorn,

> No leaves it has, no prickly points;
> It is a mass of knotted joints,
> A wretched thing forlorn,

and every season it looks more disreputable and
more dissipated.

In contrast to these, there is a group of plants
which flourish exceedingly for a while, and spread
ravishingly about the garden; after some years they
diminish and finally disappear, and no matter how
often re-introduced, refuse to repeat their first
delightful performance. I fancy that the species
which do this vary to some extent in different districts; with me *Linaria alpina* and *Papaver alpinum*
were noteworthy instances. The meaning of this
phenomenon has always puzzled me. One theory
is that the plant exhausts a certain quality of the
soil; that seems unlikely. Is there a diminution in
vigour in the successive generations, just as, in the
case of some newly introduced species, there appears
to be an increase, or at least a change rendering
them more suited to the new conditions?

Again, there is the question of slugs, a race which
has more murders to its discredit than the worst of
the Cæsars or Borgias. But here again there is

discrimination.   Not only are some slugs more
destructive than others (one species, indeed, preys
upon its fellows, and ought to be encouraged, like
those of the genus Testacella which live on earth-
worms), but they attack different plants in different
gardens.   There are some plants, indeed, which are
gobbled everywhere unless protected, like *Phyteuma
comosum*; but many others are persistently eaten
in some places, and never even nibbled in others
—another phenomenon worthy of investigation. Of
one thing, however, we may be sure—slugs will
always tackle a new plant, and the rarer it is the
greater their anxiety to sample it.   Mortality may be
reduced considerably by putting a zinc ring round
every new small prize: it will keep off not only
slugs, but many things besides.

I find I have been prowling round the fringes of
my subject, between the living and the dead, without the courage to enter the main cemetery at all.
But it is before my eyes all the time, populous with
lost treasures—Primulas and Gentians by the dozen,
dainty alpine Androsaces and Campanulas and
Phyteumas, stiff little Lewisias, and silvery tiny
Artemisias; Æthionemas, Violas, Pentstemons, and
what not.   Each for a while has gladdened my
heart,

> . . . and anon
> Like snow upon the desert's dusty face
> Lighting a little hour or two—is gone.

Things from Chili and from China, whose want of
hardiness was conveniently excused in nursery-
men's lists; North American plants, whose need of

peat was modestly concealed; high alpine gems that
even under the most skilled treatment are short-
lived in our uncongenial lowland gardens, though
venerable with age among the snowy crags; each in
his narrow cell for ever laid, is now but a memory.
But experience brings wisdom to all who know
how to learn, and knowledge foreshadows success;
many deaths have been redeemed by subsequent
success.   There is no use trying to grow a difficult plant till you have found out all you can about
it—what country it comes from, what climate,
what elevation—if possible, what soil.   Then you
will have something to go upon—some idea
where and how to plant it.   But for all rock plants
(and it is they in particular of which I am thinking),
deep drainage above all things, and a light soil.   And
there are two fortuitous and unsightly aids which
will save many a life: one is the zinc ring already
mentioned; the other is for the woolly-leaved
treasures that damp off in our abominable winters
—a triangular piece of glass pushed into the earth
close to the plant at an angle of 45°, so as to form a
kind of roof.   This has a surprising effect on such
things as *Asperula Athoa* and the tiny Androsaces.

But many of the loveliest of the mountain nymphs
will not come to us: it is we who must go to them,
to the infinite benefit of both mind and body. There,
on the wide-flung crags, to see them is an education
in itself, and brings an uplifting of the heart such as
few things can give; but in our gardens they languish
and pine, and in spite of all our loving care, one
day we find them gone. *Requiescant in pace*!

B. & I.

It began at the Dublin Zoo one morning in October. There was a commotion among the polar bears, audible over the length and breadth of the gardens. Hurrying up to see the fun, I found Francis Dixon feeding them with crab-apples. An apple had dropped into their bath; they were simultaneously trying to grab it, one from either side, and each was saying to the other, "I beg your pardon," in a tone that reverberated through the Phœnix Park. The incongruity of a squabble over a crab-apple between these huge flesh-eaters was so comical that when, on the path by the lake, we encountered the big sea-lion having a stroll like ourselves, it seemed quite in the nature of things. He had discovered a sub-aqueous ingress to the tank next to his own, and from there had leaped the railings and gained his freedom—but that is a detail: the point was that here he strolled, waddling and grunting along like a stout elderly stockbroker. Then in the Reptile House we inspected, without mishap, the horned toads, that shoot drops of blood at you out of their eyes, and felt that we were returning to normality. That concluded the first episode.

The same afternoon, at a neighbour's house, I heard a small friend, clothed chiefly in stockings and a large blue bow, reciting her "piece":—

"Autumn leaves are falling, falling
Autumn birds are calling, calling."

As I walked home the melancholy couplet went round and round in endless iteration, as persistent as Mark Twain's " Punch, brothers, punch with care." And that was the second noteworthy event of the day, as the sequel showed.

I had to cross to Liverpool that night. It was blowing hard from the east, with white-topped waves even in the Liffey, and the uneasy motion of the steamer as I climbed the gangway recalled the rolling gait of the sea-lion. One could look forward with confidence to a lively night of it. Early bed, before the " Lady Louth " got into the free swing of the Irish Sea, seemed desirable.

*   *   *   *   *

Dr. Ferrar was explaining that polar bears live habitually on crab-apples and custard-apples, for which they climb icy cliffs in Spitsbergen, when there was a roar from the beasts, and with a crash the cage fell to pieces. A swaying bar of yellow light shot across above me. Aurora borealis? No, it was the ceiling of the state-room swaying drunkenly. From every side came a chorus of noises, a babel that might have put to shame the combined efforts of Mr. Blythe's numismatic menagerie—all the old familiar voices that accompany the short Channel sea when it is joyously dancing to an October gale, and the wind is screaming in the rigging. There is not one bull, but several at least, all roaring; and as for pigs, the whole litter fully grown could not make their presence more audible. There are other more distressful sounds, too, that one associates with human beings who wish they could die, but cannot, and a vague loud howling noise, like some large creature in pain.

> Through the midnight sailing, sailing,
> Polar bears are wailing, wailing——

Confound the thing! ... It is a head sea, which is something to the good after all—one doesn't get flung out of one's berth. Perhaps the crab-apples didn't agree with them. That swaying shadow on the wall is very like a sea-lion—or is it a tortoise—or a dragon? I am wide awake now. I fall to thinking of queer beasts of the present, and queerer beasts of the past. I try to picture that Age of Dragons, some millions of years ago, when our earth was owned by reptiles—air, land, and sea alike. I see a stormy sky full, not of birds, but of flying lizards without tails—all Prof. Seeley's "Dragons of the Air," and more—some as big as ostriches, others no larger than sparrows. And they can do what no bird can, for when they alight they run about on all fours, their leathery wings furled and tucked upwards at an angle, like the piston of George Stephenson's "Rocket." They look rather like goats with swan necks and huge crocodile heads. On the land, too, are monstrous creatures —dinosaurs and what not—of unbelievable appearance and size. There goes Atlantosaurus, heaving his vast bulk along. As he walks he leaves cavernous footprints each a square yard in size—no

wonder, for the brute weighs thirty tons. And as
to length! If he stood on his tail he might surprise
the guests in the topmost bedrooms of the
Shelbourne Hotel by smiling in at them through the
curtains—or he could look down the chimneys, for
the matter of that, if he had any interest in the
question of smoke abatement.

I fall to wondering what was the sudden mishap
that buried the dinosaurs' eggs, whose discovery in
Central Asia, fossilized but unbroken, gave the
newspapers such good (but only half exploited) copy
a few years ago. Was it flood—or dust-storm?
And what did the mother dinosaurs do about it?
The only answer that comes is the crash of heavy
seas falling aboard, and the long following hiss of
water swishing along the deck. Other more
mysterious sounds mingle too—an intermittent
deep boom or roar, like a gigantic last trump, and
from further away incessant short screaming sounds,
like all the yelping devils behind the Pilgrims'
Chorus in Tannhäuser. I keep assuring myself that
I feel quite comfortable. My mind, dwelling on the
Zoo and its queer inmates, pauses at a dramatic
" fossil event " recently brought to light on Tenerife
—the finding of the remains of many giant tortoises
huddled together among layers of lava and ash on
that volcanic island. These are now among the
rarest of the grotesque creatures of the world, for
their longevity—they live for a couple of centuries
or so—has been of no avail against that destructive
creature man. But in old days giant tortoises lived
on that Atlantic peak. I try to reconstruct the final

scene—catastrophic eruptions, clouds of dust and steam, rivers of molten lava: these terrified dumb monsters crawling together for safety on an island in the lava stream, and there perishing miserably —not by the lava itself, which would have reduced their skeletons to ashes, but by boiling mud perhaps, or clouds of poisonous gas. The vision of their grotesque forms stumbling about in a sulphurous smother becomes a nightmare, and I try to think of daylight, and Lime-street station, and the breakfast-car on the London train.

I must have gone to sleep then, as all I can recall of the next couple of hours is that the sea-lion asked me to recite to him, and the only lines I could remember were:

> There was never a light in the sky that night
>   of the soft midsummer gales.
> But the great man-bloaters snorted low,
>   and the young 'uns sang like whales.

And the sea-lion's moustaches twitched, and in an agonized voice he called " Steward!"

*   *   *   *   *

Crash! That was a big one! The steamer seems to pause and remain quite still for a moment, as if to recover, while from a distance comes the tinkle of falling glass. The land must be a thousand miles away. How many people on board are asleep? I try to picture the watch on deck in that screaming black wind—all withdrawn to the shelter of the bridge. There is the first officer, but I do not see the captain among them . . .

Autumn gales are roaring, roaring.
Captain Blank is snoring, snoring.

Oh, confound it! I must be snoozing again. Then comes a thrill of surprise, for out of a long stretch of palm-trees there glides a flying thing undreamed of by Darwin or Audubon. With horror I recognise that astonishing creature, by Flamingo out of Sea-Anemone, whiffling over tulgy beds of iris and lupin (or is it purple loosestrife?), whose rainbow presence perturbs the after-dinner meditations of life-members at chamber concerts at Ballsbridge. It circles round, while deathly silence falls, and I try to crawl under a queer snake-like plant that writhes over the sand. Then everything is dark, but still I crouch paralysed. How long in that same trance I lay I have not to declare, but at length there comes from an infinite distance the irregular tolling of a bell.

Lady Louth is rolling, rolling,
Passing bells are tolling, tolling.

It passes sure enough, fading in long-drawn diminuendo; then, quite suddenly, as it seems, we are in calmer water, and a cheerful voice in the passage says something about a buoy.

When next I become conscious of any definite environment a steward is standing with a cup of tea on a little tray. I look at him hard to make sure he is not a penguin, for I have been jerked back from antarctic ice-fields, and his white shirt-front is ambiguous; but the " B. & I." monogram on the purple lapel of his jacket is reassuring. " Off New Brighton, sir." From the porthole one has a vignette of yellow-grey mist half hiding the heaving water and ships and warehouses. The sun is up, and it gilds, high above the fog, the great birds on the pinnacles of the Liver Building; but they recall the Basilisk of Ballsbridge, and with a shudder I drop my eyes to the muddy water, and the swaying ferryboats, and the " Graphic " ahead of us edging in to the landing-stage, her red funnel glowing through the smoke like a pillar of fire beckoning us on to the promised land.

SPELEOLOGICA.

SPELEOLOGY is the science and study of caves. The subject should have some interest to us in Ireland, for this country is essentially a land of caves of many kinds, and stands pre-eminent in this respect in Europe.

All caves, in the ordinary sense, can be divided into three groups, and each of these has originated in a quite different way. First there are the artificial caverns or " souterrains," remarkably abundant in Ireland, and often found within the confines of earthen raths—caves excavated in gravel or clay, lined with field stones, roofed with slabs, and often containing several small chambers. These are the work of early, but not very early, man, and if we dig in their floors we find human relics mostly of the Iron Age—Early Christian or pre-Christian. Next there are the sea-caves, distributed around the coast, and formed by compressed air working along fissures in the rock under the influence of heavy waves. These are picturesque features of our cliff-bound shores, with a romantic tang about them of smugglers and mermaids and pirates. Their mode of origin tends to the production of mostly straight and horizontal passages of no very great length. Sometimes their position with relation to present sea-level furnishes the geologist with valuable evidence as to the raising or lowering of coast-lines by local earth-movement—for " terra firma " is a restless and unstable medium, seldom at peace. The third kind of caves is the most important. These are formed in rocks which are soluble, by the action of running water. Limestone and rock-salt furnish examples of such material, and almost all the great caves of the world, including those of this country, are formed in limestone. To understand their peculiar topography we have to recall the history of limestone. Long ago, at various geological periods, circumstances have favoured the laying down on the sea-bottom of deep beds of limy mud, resulting mainly from the decay of the shells of countless millions of minute animals. In the course of ages, these muds have become consolidated into beds of limestone, which, still showing clearly the lines of the original stratification, now lie piled one above another. But earth-movements have often disturbed their horizontality, so that now they frequently slope, or even stand vertical. Cracks have developed within the beds, often in two series at right-angles to the bedding and to each other, so that the rock tends to become a complex of rectangular blocks. Water, falling as rain, trickles down and along these cracks. Now, water with a trace of acid in it can dissolve limestone, and as some acid is usually present, the cracks get enlarged until eventually a considerable stream may flow far underground, continuing to excavate for itself a larger and still larger tunnel, and at intervals forsaking an old channel for a more newly-formed lower one. Since the joints along which the caves are excavated may be in three different planes, these caves of solution are not, like sea-caves, simply more or less level passages, but may go in any direction—up or down, right or left, and often branching. A stream running through the fields may abruptly drop down a hundred-foot-deep crack, then run underground in a devious course for miles, and re-issue as a gigantic spring or leap out of an arch in a waterfall. Caves open to the air have since early times furnished convenient natural houses for wild beasts and for primitive man; and their floors, often cemented by layers of stalagmite, with beds of mud and sand between, are a fruitful field for the zoological and archæological explorer. It was in the floor deposits of a small cave of this kind in Waterford that a party of diggers lately discovered the first undoubted relics of Palæolithic man in Ireland—there lay the skeletons, preserved in stalagmite, and surrounded by bones of the contemporary and now extinct animals which lived in the Magdelenian period, many thousands of years ago.

But your true speleologist does not worry about the remains that may lie entombed in cave-deposits. His interest is in the caves themselves, their mode of formation, their complicated geography, and he devotes his energies to exploring and mapping them. And this surveying is a much more energetic and difficult pursuit than might be imagined. First, there is the point that one is working in black darkness—not the darkness of a starless winter night, but *absolute* darkness, a velvety blackness which you might cut with a knife, and in which a candle shines like a sun. Next, one is working in three dimensions, not in two, as is usual on the surface of the Earth. Abysses may yawn which have to be descended by means of rope ladders lashed end to end—often, indeed, by merely a single rope, on the end of which the seeker after truth dangles like a spider, until his observations allow the more cumbrous but safer rope ladder to be fixed. After that the course may be up or down, this way or that, over or under vast fallen blocks, through passages two feet—or two hundred—wide or high, round angle after angle till one's sense of direction is utterly lost, and one has to work by compass.

Then again, while the majority of known caves consist of tunnels which the water has now abandoned, in many others the streams which formed them are still in occupation. At the Marble Arch at Florencecourt, in Fermanagh, a swim of a hundred yards or so was necessary to reach the upper part of the cave until one day, exploring among dense hazel scrub on the hill above, we stumbled on a chasm full of great moss-grown boulders. Worming in through and under these (feeling like small flies in a bowl of lump sugar) we found a passage leading downwards, which after twists and drops and unprobed expansions led us (to our astonishment) to the upper end of the Marble Arch underground lake. This was a relief, for cave water is icy cold, and to swim or splutter along with a candle in one's hat, and knife-edges of rock rising out of deep, inky water, on the chance of finding a practicable cave floor at the other end, requires faith and agility. More often than not, in these flooded caves

the roof slowly descends towards the water, and
eventually passes below it, and if there is a current,
one may be in danger of being sucked under, and
good-bye to further cave work.

At another spot in the Florencecourt area a
stream plunges into a small opening in the ground
known as Noon's Hole. Cautious exploration
showed that the chasm was of great depth. The
question of the falling water was a trouble, for one
must stand under a waterfall—a very small one
will suffice—to realise the weight and sting of the
water which looks so light and fleecy as it descends
in spray through the air. Finally, we dammed the
stream with sods, and anxiously buttressed up our
dam while an explorer descended hurriedly on a
rope, with a life-line in his hands to steady him.
Eventually this " swallow-hole " proved to be a
hundred and fifty feet deep.

Caves still or till recent times in process of formation are often much choked with mud and rubbish
and full of sharp rock-edges, and as the mud is often
slippery and dangerous, and the rock-edges can cut
like knives, they are not popular with the speleologist. The caves that he loves are those long since
derelict by streams, for there the slow dripping of
limy water has encased roof, walls, and floor alike
in gleaming crystalline stalagmite and stalactite of a
thousand fantastic forms and hues—curtains and
columns and arches and terraces of white or creamy
rock, forming scenery of a type undreamed of and
unknown elsewhere on or in our many-featured
planet. The fantastic beauty of such grottoes has

long been a theme of both romance and science. Our modern race of showmen light them up with coloured electric lamps, and exhaust their vocabulary in inventing names for their more striking features; but even in our own country beautiful stalactite-draped caverns, seldom if ever entered by man, still await the enterprising, and their discovery is the reward of the speleologist.

Most of our larger Irish caves have now been explored, and some of them mapped, often under circumstances of considerable difficulty, for the traversing and surveying of such rough and often dangerous ground by the light of candles is not easy. But a prismatic compass and tape, combined with experience and determination, will do wonders. In essence, you set up two candles, measure the distance between them, and take the compass bearing of one with regard to the other, and simply continue this process, subsequently laying down these lines on paper according to their length and direction; but in practice the difficulties which intervene are innumerable, and all the while there is the handicap of the darkness.

Looked on as a sport, there is no pastime which needs more enterprise or more caution than speleology, and certainly none which so exercises every muscle of the body. At one time one is clambering over or under great blocks of rock in a vast hall; at another one is faced with places like the " Rabbit-hole " in Mitchelstown Cave. Here a huge block has subsided, stopping the passage, but under it is a mere crevice, two feet wide and one and a half high, through which one works on one's back, till it turns vertically upwards and at the same time reverses its dimensions: the passage of that angle is a test of one's suppleness and courage, for to feel the pressure of the rock on every side of one's body is disconcerting to the beginner. Then, after strenuous hours amid the strangest scenery, in utter darkness and stillness, and no trace of life, save the rare presence of spiders or insects specially adapted for cave life, comes the return to the surface: the first blue gleam of distant daylight, finally the blessed (and blinding) sunlight, the sight of green fields, the surprising modelling of hill and dale, and all the joyful motion and colour of sky and air and land.

This " New Cave " of Mitchelstown, which is the best known of Irish caverns, and till recently was reckoned the longest cave in the British Isles (its passages total $1\frac{3}{4}$ miles) is well worth the attention of the passing traveller; while its complete exploration needs full equipment, much can be seen by the ordinary visitor under proper guidance. But a still longer cave, as yet only partially known, is that at the base of Slieve Elva in Clare. The passages in it are unusually level, but they are still occupied by streams, and this combined with the low height of the roof in the further parts makes grave difficulties for the visitor. Recent explorers—two Englishmen —narrate how they climbed and waded and occasionally swam and finally crawled on all fours in the stream with the roof scraping their backs, until at a point two miles from the entrance they had to give up, having reached the limit of human endur-

ance. They describe the cave as full of beautiful
and interesting features in the portion traversed,
and it continues, no one knows how far, beyond the
point reached by Messrs. Baker and Barton. What
Irishman will carry on the exploration?

IN TIROL.

How many ants are there in Tirol? Here, as in every spot where we lie down, they may be safely reckoned at five to the square foot. That, on a conservative estimate, would give a hundred thousand millions (or 10^{11}, as the mathematician would more succinctly express it) for the whole province, one and undivided as it used to be and ought to be ... We are sprawling in a dry pine wood on the edge of a vast gorge, and the heat that impels in us a contemplative laziness urges to fresh exertions the myriad ants, large and small, yellow, brown, and black. Their industry is appalling, and it is redoubled when we begin feeding them with bread-crumbs; with an activity which is merely delirious they carry them along a well-tramped ant-road which eventually reaches their city, a five-foot heap of dead twigs and leafy fragments thirty feet away. The butterflies, too, invite consideration; through the dappled glades they flicker everywhere—several kinds, but mostly a very dark one, nearly black, with brown spots; and like Crusoe's beasts, their tameness is shocking to us, for they will not let us have our lunch. At the moment, my companion has two on her hat, one on either hand, one on the sandwich which she is endeavouring to eat, and one on the tip of her nose. Nor is this unusual domesticity confined to one sort of butterfly: two other kinds hover round us, or open and shut their wings as they perch on a convenient elbow or shoulder. In this delightful country all the creatures, indeed, are as friendly as the genial Tirolese and the crowd of happy visitors. The graceful cattle rub their heads against you lazily when you put an arm round their necks, just as a cat might do; and high up on a patch of snow and rock a crowd of sheep and lambs mob me ecstatically, even to the extent of springing on my shoulders; they think apparently that I have something nice for them—sugar-candy, perhaps. Down in our hotel, a great sixteenth century gabled house with vaulted stone ceilings not only on the ground floors, but upstairs also, the hall is hung with heads and horns, trophies of local prowess. Swallows have built nests between each pair of supporting antlers, and all day long they fly to and fro above the hats of the moving folk below. In the early morning, too, they skim into our room and hover twittering over the bed before darting out again. These mornings in Mauterndorf indeed are lively, for hourly Masses in the old church close by begin disconcertingly at four o'clock, and the bells, much more melodious than those of our country, ring not only before Mass, but take part in the service at frequent intervals—tending to early rising or to malediction, as the case may be. By five the village street is lively with both peasants and visitors: by six, breakfast is ready for those who are capable of appreciating the best hours of the long summer days. One leans out of the window and tries to tell the time from the great clock-face a hundred feet above the street; but the long spidery hands have a big golden blob at either end, and as one half of each hand is nearly as extended as the other, a considerable choice of hours offers itself. No matter; the sun is rising and the air is like champagne; let us be up and away. The forests that tower steeply for three thousand feet are wreathed in mist, and the snows above still retain a trace of their pink morning blush. At the door the porter is already sunning himself. His dress proclaims both his nationality and his profession. Heavy clamped mountain boots, with socks rolled down over their tops; bare bronzed legs; embroidered leather shorts; a brief jacket of a loud red and black check over an open white shirt; crowning all, a black hotel-porter's cap *de rigueur,* and across its front the legend "Hotel Post" in golden letters that shine like an oriflamme in the morning glow. Out into the cheerful street, where everyone, man, woman, and child, has a cheerful "Grüss Gott" for everyone else, and so into the darkness of the pines, and up, up, up, through miles of larch and spruce and beech, till at length the trees become few and gnarled and stunted, and we emerge on the lovely alpine meadows or on slopes covered as far as eye can reach with the rosy dwarf rhododendron.

Then there are the larger hotels, as in the Dolomites, filled with a lusty throng of Austrians, Italians, Germans, Czecho-Slovaks. Let us eat, drink, and be merry is their holiday motto. The Germans are the quietest, the Italians the reverse; sit near a table where a dozen Italians are supping and you cannot hear yourself shout. And against this the utter stillness in the great forests at noon; not a bird's note, not a stir of the branches; only the faint hum of innumerable insects, and far away the sound of falling water. And above the forest limit, naked and stark, rise the tremendous dolomite crags, like vast cathedrals a mile in height, with a hundred spires and pinnacles; round their base grim grey screes, a thousand feet high, guard the approach, and far up, small glaciers huddle in deep ravines. These astonishing hills are ever a wonder and a delight: in the morning silver-grey, at sunset glowing rich rosy red; and ever preserving an attitude of austere dignity and remoteness that leaves one without words.

We wander on into lovely regions beyond the ken of the British tourist; in four weeks we meet only two English people, and in the same time not once do we hear an American accent. The latter is a relief, for on the Hook steamer and in Holland we encountered so potent a brew of young America that we fled by aeroplane from their painted faces and nasal ecstatics, nor paused until we dropped down on Innsbruck. Then the Brenner took us into southern Tirol, with its Austrian population and Italian officials; where the station-master blandly professes not to understand you unless you mention a place by its Italian name (not given on most available maps) and the hills are filled with *Alpini*, who spend their time dragging machine-guns and soup buckets up impossible precipices, and then bringing them down again, shouting, singing, and laughing the while. On eastward along the lovely Pustertal, and up the side valleys towards the snows of the

Gross-Glockner and Gross-Venediger. You do your
climbing by stages here, with a pleasant hotel at
every stage. The panting train from Vienna drops
you somewhere in the main valley; a narrow-gauge
line wriggles up another thousand feet; thence a
post-auto lifts you a further two thousand, as far as
the *baumgrenze*—the tree-limit; and then you climb
up flowery mountain paths two or three thousand
feet more, to the very edge of the eternal snow,
where lonely tourist huts stand sentinel, and cheerful peasant girls serve you a hot meal, excellent in
quality—and wonderfully cheap, considering that
everything, including the fuel, has to be carried up
on men's backs from the valley far below.

We push further eastward, into Styria and Car-
inthia, where Byzantine influence begins to make
itself felt; but still the mountains continue, a limit-
less sea of lovely hills, inviting a life-time of exploration. Oh! the joy and beauty of it all! The intoxi-
cating nip in the air, the wonder of rock and glacier,
the gem-like alpine flowers, the piping hot coffee,
the piercing brilliance of the stars at night; the start
at early morning, with the upland meadows grey
with frost; the dim aisles of the woods; the hot
midday sun; the long afternoon rest, with the mar-
mots whistling at you from the mouths of their
burrows. The courteous welcome at the inn; the
less formal departure, where everyone, from pro-
prietor to kitchen-maid, must shake hands with you
and wish you " Glückliche Reise" and " Auf Wieder-
sehen." The thunder-storm in the hills at night,
lighting up the glaciers momentarily with a ghastly

white glare, while the thunder crashes from cliff to cliff and from mountain to mountain; and in the morning everything glistening after the rain, and fresh flower-gems opening in each rock crevice.

On the last evening before turning our faces westward, we sit in a mountain hut on the edge of a high cliff. Three thousand feet below twinkle the lights of the village we have left—so close under us that one might imagine that one could toss a stone on the tiled roof of the church. The girls who have attended to our wants have a zither, and in small pure voices they sing old Styrian melodies, and play laments and tinkling dances, and strange airs unlike our western music, while a cold wind howls outside, and at intervals comes the distant carillon of the cow-bells. Heigh-ho! to-morrow to Berlin for the "conning of plant-mummies" in the Museum, and then across the monotonous North German plain towards England.

DIESE VERDAMMTEN UNKRAÜTER.

WHEN one sets out to write about weeds after two most wet and weedful seasons, it is difficult to find an adjective which to the gardener appears adequate, and at the same time does not hurt delicate susceptibilities; under the circumstances it may be wise to fall back for a title on some language other than English.

For two years now, indeed, we have been fairly snowed under; the wicked have flourished exceedingly; and many a stalwart gardener, surveying a sea of Groundsel, Chickweed, and Willowherb, has thrown up his hands in despair. Carramba! what a wilderness. And yet these weeds, philosophically considered, have many points of interest and are worthy of our attention, if only to discover how best to counter their unending activity. Here at once is a point for discussion. How does it come about that, despite our every effort at extermination, the weeds, like a plague of locusts, still march forward in their thousands, rioting and massacreing as they go? Most of the plants which we grow and tend plod quietly on without much increase; others we have trouble in keeping alive at all; but the weeds! This question carries with it different answers according to the kind of weed we are dealing with. The worst weeds of all, the ones which it is practically impossible to exterminate, are those which have perennial creeping underground stems

—" creeping roots," to use the common phrase. Couch-grass, Colt's-foot, Bindweed are three notorious examples. The underground stems are usually formed of a series of short joints, just as aerial stems and branches are; these joints give out roots, or are capable of doing so (as the joints of aerial stems do when grown as cuttings); and they are also capable of producing fresh shoots, like those of aerial branches. In consequence, every joint—and there may be a dozen to a foot of stem—is a potential new plant; and every scrap of stem left in the ground helps to render fruitless our war of extermination. Again, their rapid growth soon takes these underground stems into every part of the garden or bed; and no matter how much we clear the ground, there are always some spots—among the roots of a shrub or in a box-edging—which we cannot dig; there our enemy lies, and from these foci he reconquers rapidly his lost territory. Continual digging and cleaning, with the fork rather than the spade, is the best recipe; but there is another mode of attack. The vigour, the very life of these subterranean stems depends on the food manufactured by the green leaves above. If we can strike at the food supply we shall cripple the enemy; if we can cut it off effectually, we shall kill him. A field can be entirely cleared of Bracken by *frequent* scything down of the young fronds as they appear, carried on through one or at the most two seasons. Bindweed growing among shrubs, where it cannot be got at, may be at least greatly diminished by the pulling of every shoot that appears. The main point is to give no respite, no opportunity of recovery; it is carelessness in this respect that often leads to failure.

But it is not this class of weeds which has been plaguing us, especially in the recent wet seasons; it is the annuals. These annual plants have none of the subterranean organisation of Couch-grass or Colt's-foot. They are light rooters, easily removed. How do they contrive an equally successful and outrageous defiance of all our attacks upon them? Simply by the sound business expedient of a quick turn-over, coupled with the fact that our mild climate allows them to grow, to flower, and to seed practically the whole twelve months. That is why they have got out of all bounds in these years of mild winters and wet summers. They have never ceased growing, generation after generation. Some of them are aided by special contrivances in connection with the dispersal of their seed. While Chickweed, with a false modesty, simply allows its seed to fall on the earth below, the little Hairy Cress wickedly shoots out its seeds to a distance of several feet. This is accomplished by the unequal shrinking, when ripe, of the slender pods in which the seeds are contained. Stresses are set up which eventually cause the pod to rupture with a snap, flinging the seeds violently out. The Groundsel and Willowherb, on the other hand, belong to the very interesting group of plants which have parachute seeds. The tiny germ is firmly enclosed in a woody box, representing the lower part of the calyx, and the upper part of the calyx is converted into a beautiful plume of silky hairs. The large surface which these hairs offer allows the wind readily to carry them away, and also causes them to fall slowly in the air; so they can be borne considerable distances. One disturbing feature of this ease of dispersal is that Groundsel in one's neighbour's garden is almost as great a threat as Groundsel in one's own. But it is the rapid " turn-over " mainly that gives the annual weeds their advantage. Neglect a plot for only a month, and hey presto! the Groundsel has already grown and flowered and scattered its thousands of flying seeds far and wide. Against these weeds the battle-cry is obvious—don't let them seed. Hoe, and hoe, and hoe, while they are young.

The Mountain Willowherb, that shameless squatter, has a different story. Its erect stems, clothed with opposite pairs of leaves, bear small pink flowers which are quickly succeeded by long slender pods, from which issues a cloud of exceptionally light parachute seeds, capable of extended flight. Then, at the base of the stem two buds form, which, as autumn approaches, root firmly in the ground while the parent stem fades, and form the plant of the succeeding season. In hand-weeding, the important thing in this case is to weed not later than the flowering of the plant (June-July). Thus we not only prevent seeding, but the young shoots at the base come away with the stem, and so the whole plant is destroyed. If we wait too long, till August or September, only the old stem comes away, and the plant goes uninjured.

Just one more miscreant. Consider that sedate person, the Dandelion. He takes no risks. Under his rosette of toothed leaves a tap-root, fat with stored food, goes down a foot or more (in dry places), to reach the moister layers of soil. His golden blossom is made up of a hundred flowers, collected into a single bloom—an economical and efficient concentration; it is succeeded by a globe of the most dainty and fairy-like parachutes, at the lower end of each of which a single seed is suspended. If Dandelions were as rare as Edelweiss, how we would admire them and cherish them. As it is, they are a confounded pest —out with them! More easily said than done, for the long tap-roots are difficult to remove, and are possessed of great vitality. Dig them in, and the leaves will eventually struggle up to the surface, though they may have to force their way through a foot of soil. Chop them up, and some of the pieces at least will sprout and form new plants. So treat the Dandelion as a worthy enemy; dig him right out and burn him, and do this before he gets a chance of launching his fairy parachutes. But his brigand-age need not blind us to his beauty. One morning I stood in a mountain orchard on the frontier of Bohemia. Under the canopy of fragrant apple-blossom the early sunlight dappled dewy grass so thickly interspersed with grey globes of Dandelion seed that a light gleaming mist seemed to hover over the ground. And I said (being a safe thousand miles away from my own garden), Thank God for the Dandelion! Even though I am a gardener, I can say that still.

HOMEWARD BOUND.

THE agent at San Sebastian had told us that a steamer of his line would call at Hermigua on on Wednesday, bound for Tenerife; but his deputy in the creeper-covered house there shrugs his shoulders and spreads his hands. The steamer may come—or it may not; the higher powers alone know. This does not suit us at all, for our English liner, homeward-bound, leaves Santa Cruz on Saturday. We have no desire to be marooned here on Gomera, even though it is, perhaps, the loveliest and most interesting of the Canary Archipelago. We have now been wandering over the seven islands for three months—on foot, on mules, in motors, on camels: across deserts, through forests, lava-flows, gigantic craters, enormous precipices. We have slept on sea-sands, in smart hotels, in ploughed fields, in village guest-rooms insectiferous beyond belief. We are as thin as whipping-posts and as brown as chocolate, and our clothes—the less said about them the better. We have come to feel at home among the easy-going, friendly island-folk, but now Ireland is calling, and the mañana habit no longer appeals. Enquiry reveals a small fruit steamer, leaving for Santa Cruz at sunset. A bargain is soon struck, and as evening falls we descend the steep valley to the sea, the 2,000-foot cliffs blue with shadow below, burning red with the sunset at their summits. Our way leads through banana-groves, and along a stony beach where the Atlantic surf thunders. Below the black cliff, on the right hand, a low rock rises from deep water. On this a high tower of concrete and steel has been raised. From a kind of eagle's nest on the cliff, approached by a buttressed road, a great lattice-girder runs out, is supported mid-way by the tower, and projects far over the ocean. We step into a sort of crate slung below the girder, are propelled out to its dizzy extremity, and dropped a hundred feet down to sea-level, where, by a well-timed jerk, we are dumped into a waiting boat as she rises to the swell, and are paddled to our rolling steamer. No companion-ladder here. Two hairy pirates lean far over the side, and as our boat surges upward we are caught by the wrists and hauled up and across the gunwale. An impression of brown faces, a narrow, grimy deck, a mountain of banana cases. Then another pirate, wearing a yachting cap to mark his captain's rank, leads us up to the tiny bridge, where we are allotted a free space about six feet by three for dining-room and drawing-room. Forward, banana boxes, beyond which rises the disdainful face of a camel. Aft, more banana boxes. Our siren blows, and the long wail echoes and re-echoes from the towering cliffs. The crane-man replies with a screech from the whistle of his engine, and we are off. The telegraph signals full speed. The machinery groans and wheezes, and we waddle along the cliffs at a six-knot gait with the swell behind us.

To the eastward Tenerife stretches, a dream-island, its precipices and peaks glowing a soft brick-red in the sunset, pink cloud-wreaths wrapping the higher parts, and Pico del Teyde towering to over 12,000 feet, far above the highest clouds. To the west, Gomera is dark in shadow.

It is a windless evening, and the long swell is oily and blue-grey, reflecting from a thousand facets the orange and crimson of the sunset. The captain opines that it is supper-time, and sets down among us a case of bananas by way of table. We produce bread and fruit, which we have had the foresight to bring with us. From a cubby-hole below us there is a flash of white teeth; " pescado," says the cook, and passes up a broiled fish. (He drops the " s," Canary-fashion, so that it sounds like a confession of sin.) Delicious coffee follows—in the Canaries the dirtiest little den that ever miscalled itself a restaurant will produce coffee such as in Ireland you may dream of, but never find. Darkness falls while we eat, and the intense heat of the day gives way to a delicious coolness. A long, drowsy silence succeeds, and presently bed is suggested.

In a tiny, stuffy four-berth cabin two school-boys are fast asleep in one bed; the other three invite us, and we crawl in. The woodwork is painted white; a small lamp glimmers. Distant snores keep time with the thump-thump of the engine.

Is it imagination, or are all those dim black things above my head really moving? A voice breaks in: " Will you hand me up my slipper?" Talk of Thermopylae! I can see better now; we are experienced in the island fauna, and I watch with a detached interest the voyages of discovery of innumerable creatures. " That one with the sprint is the oriental cockroach," I find myself muttering, " but what the dickens are the other two?" A question never answered.

The heat, not the many-legged companions, renders sleep impossible, and presently I wander back to our perch on the bridge. The little ship rolls easily along, every wave that she throws off glowing with phosphorescence. Far to the left the lighthouse on the western end of Tenerife twinkles, and to the right the light near San Sebastian, on Gomera. The sky overhead is velvet blue, and in it the stars blaze as they never do in Ireland. Over the southern horizon Canopus, unseen in our northern latitudes, burns steadily.

Save for the glimmer of the binnacle lamp, all is dark on board. The steersman, a black silhouette, begins to sing. This Canarian singing, which we often heard echoing across the mountain valleys, is very interesting. The singer pours out his soul in long recitative in a minor key, with characteristic trills and turns. The voices are mostly harsh, but not unpleasing, though sometimes it is shouting rather than singing; and there is a wild abandon about it that is in keeping with the country and the people. My songster sings of women. His sweethearts—he has plenty of them, it would seem—are extolled in turn. Juanita, Mariquita, Dolores—each gets her meed of praise; her eyes, her hair, her dress are celebrated in song.

For twenty minutes the recital goes on. Then

silence, only broken by the soft swish of the waves and the snoring of the camel-men lying among the banana boxes on the forward deck. With a resounding snort a great sea-beast close alongside rolls over and disappears in a welter of phosphorescence.

Silence falls again, till the singer, who has been whistling softly, lifts his voice once more. This time he sings of all the countries which he has visited, or of which he has heard. La bella España, of course, comes first—its beautiful cities, its mountains, its brave people. Alemaña follows and gets a full share, for there has been and still is much intercourse between Germany and the Canaries. Francia gets her meed of praise, and Italia. Of Ingleterra the singer appears less sure. England is a queer place, it would seem; and when he gets to Scandinavia our helmsman has clearly lost control of his ship. The song goes on and on. A new lighthouse appears ahead. " Punta del Socorro," calls the helmsman. A dancing red meteor resolves itself into the stump of a cigar as a dim shadow steps up to relieve the wheel.

We are under the shelter of Tenerife now, and it is very calm and still. The hours drift by. A star has set, a star has risen. Were it not for the murmur at the bows, one might fancy that one could hear, like Alfred Noyes' tramp,

> " A funny, silent sound, sir,
> Mixed with curious crackles in a steady undertone,
> Just the sound of twenty billion stars a-going round, sir."

Dancing lights appear on the ocean in front. As we
drift past them they are seen to be torches in boats
where men are fishing.

At last a faint glow in the east tells of approaching
day. The dawn shows the long southern coast of
Tenerife stretching mile upon mile close on the
port bow, with little villages dotted on the steep
slopes, from sea-level up to three thousand feet,
where the cloud-wreaths hang. Soon these catch
the sun, and through them we get glimpses of golden
uplands, while the lower grounds are flecked with
light.

At five o'clock my companions join me, in time
to see the sun rise out of the sea. Simultaneously,
coffee appears. The camel-men stir, and look round
sleepily; day has begun. For many hours more we
saunter along the coast; past Güimar, perched high
on the hillside, past Punta del Socorro, past San Isidro.

It is nearing mid-day, and the sun is blazing hot,
before we round the breakwater at Santa Cruz. Our
tortoise crawls in through the shipping, and berths
just under the stern of the " Alondra," which is to
take us to England. Three of our swarthy pirates
seize our luggage—like ourselves, much the worse
for wear—and carry it on board. On the promenade
deck we are confronted by an immaculate steward,
who regards us with dismay. " Will you look after
these things for a while," I say, " we are sailing
with you to-morrow?" He hesitates. " You had
better see the chief steward "—" sir," he adds as
afterthought, in case my improbable statement
should prove to be true.

H

FROM A SMALL ROCK GARDEN.

I AM tempted to try to justify a certain untidiness —I prefer to call it a freedom of growth—which seems to me to be allowable in the rock garden. I opine that it is worth considering from what point of view one grows one's plants. That there are two points of view, in some ways opposed to each other, is clear. They may be called the Botanical and the Horticultural. According to the former, one's interest lies largely in species, developed by nature in the course of thousands of years, rather than in artificial sports and hybrids produced by the industry of the gardener; in growing the plants as nearly as possible as they grow in nature, with a minimum of disturbance or artificial aids; and in encouraging (within reasonable limits) natural spreading and seeding.

From the other point of view—what I have perhaps unjustly called the Horticultural—one's object is to grow the plants " well," i.e. as large as possible. Care is taken that the specimens do not interfere with each other or mix, and, in fact, the plants are fed and housed as a farmer might feed and house prize animals.

Now, this latter mode of treatment is quite proper where such wonderful artificial products as modern roses, sweet peas, or pansies are in question, but I hold that it is out of place in the case of alpines and rock plants. Treat artificial plants artificially by all means, but for goodness' sake treat natural plants naturally, so far as the necessary restrictions of garden conditions allow. I visited a well-known garden not long ago, where alpine plants were so overfed that it was difficult to recognise in those straggling monsters the delightful crisp tufts—just like those which they produce in their mountain homes—which they assume when *properly* grown, wedged between stones with a light soil and an exposed position.

Again, while all treasures must be carefully safeguarded against oppression, natural effects will be produced by allowing the plants to romp and mix at will, provided you stand by to see fair play. One can produce delightful mats, with blossom of some kind showing all the time, by this means. I have had, for instance, a couple of square yards of sward formed of *Acaena microphylla* with its red fruits, wild thyme, a straggling dwarf pink, and *Sedum sexangulare*—a quite delightful combination, in which all the ingredients lived happily together.

Then, as to seedlings, which often come in welcome abundance when those enemies of rock plants—the rake and hoe—are banished; think twice before you pull up any seedlings. The effect of a plant is greatly enhanced if, instead of a single specimen, you have a colony, grouped naturally. If a good thing wants to annex a bit of ground, let it annex it; remove other treasures to some different spot, in whole or part. I never pull up a seedling

till it has flowered, for, by waiting till then, one may
secure some interesting or valuable sport or hybrid;
and even then it is allowed to grow on unless it
proposes to crowd out some more valuable plant.
The general effect of this granting of self-determina-
tion is that some bits of the rock garden look like
the real rock gardens, the alpine plant associations,
of the Alps and of our own wonderful Burren—a
population of species growing as they might in
nature; but it is the plant association of a dream, a
vegetable Babel, for here are gathered together
natives of all countries—Irishmen and New Zea-
landers, dark Iberians and fair Norsemen, Canadian
backwoodsmen and unfamiliar strangers from the
frontiers of Tibet.

" NOVELTIES."

It is probably because I am interested in botany
rather than in horticulture, and consequently find
more attraction in the species which nature has
produced in fifty thousand years than in the crosses
which gardeners have produced in five minutes (by
the simple process of transferring pollen), that I
incline to look upon " Novelties " with preliminary
suspicion.   Perhaps it is also because I have tried
so many of them and found so few to be any
improvement on old and much loved favourites.
I am again thinking not of florists' " stuff," but
of material for the rock garden. Of course, many
most interesting new species have been introduced in
recent years, notably from China; but few nursery-
men can resist a new name, and so the wary gar-

dener waits till he has seen the "novelty" before ordering it at five or ten shillings. Then, again, the hybridizing stunt tends to fill catalogues with new names, though the plants have mostly but little of novelty about them. Take the nondescript army of hybrid saxifrages. Very few of them are a whit better in any way than the parents, which possess, moreover, the glamour which always appertains, and properly so, to a natural species; a creation which is bound to be an object of intense interest to the thinking man.

Darwin explained the distinctness of species and absence of intermediates by the statement that the latter tend to die out in nature. So they ought to, and the gardener will often confer a boon by assisting the process. If a dowdy pinky-yallery thing, half-way between a Kabschia and an Engleria, is the best we can do, then let us pray heaven for a wiser heart, and let the hybrid Saxes go. I know a lot of this is rank heresy, and, for the sake of provoking thought, I have pitched it in strong, but my sympathies are with Owen Seaman when he writes—

> "Howe'er it be it seems to me
> It's not important to be New,
> New art would better Nature's best,
> But Nature knows a thing or two,"

ROCK GARDEN PATHS.

Most people will admit that a gravel path is out of place in the rock garden. The surface of a rock garden should consist of either stones or plants, and

the paths should be no exception to the rule. A
neatly gravelled path recalls box edgings and rows
of wallflowers and lobelias, or green velvet lawn
with a mathematically straight edge to it—all admir-
able in their way, but the very things one wants to
get away from in the rock garden. Of course in
public places, like Kew and Glasnevin, you cannot
get away from a well-defined path; if you made the
paths part of the rock garden you would have philis-
tines tramping all over the plants and sitting on the
stones. But in the private rock garden, be it large
or small, a more natural treatment is possible. We
have alternatives—either to use slabs of stone, preferably irregular and discontinuous, or to cover the
path with carpeters; or the two plans may be combined. In either case the effect is good. Your rock
garden, instead of looking like an archipelago, with
narrow straits of gravel, stretches continuously over
its miniature hills and dales. I began with narrow
gravel paths, but soon found that plants were quite
willing to invade them and hide their nakedness.
Four species I have found especially useful, growing
away year by year, and not minding the tramping a
bit. These are: *Epilobium Hectori*, *Acæna Buchanani*, *Cotula squalida*, *Bellium bellidioides*. Each
makes a carpet of a different tint—copper, grey-
green, brown-green, and fresh green, in the order
named—and the more they are walked on the
neater their growth and the more vivid their tint.
Wild thyme, purple, pink or white, is also suitable,
and the tiny yellow-flowered Oxalis—but in some
gardens this tends to become a troublesome weed.

Several other dwarf Acænas, such as the crimson-fruited *A. microphylla*, are as useful as *A. Buchanani*, but care must be taken to use only those species which do not possess barbed seeds.

PLANTS OF THE LAWN.

My lawn measures eleven yards by four. The *raison d'être* of these dimensions is that the dining-room carpet is less than this, and my peace treaty requires that the area of the former should be greater than the area of the latter; this sounds like a Euclidian postulate, but has, in fact, a hygienic, not a mathematical basis. With my craze (as it is designated by the lady of the carpet) for introducing things everywhere, even this blob of greenery does not escape, and I have often tried to naturalize carpeting plants among the lawn grass. Why should not the lawn, especially in the vicinity of the alpine garden, suggest, if possible, something like an alpine sward, full of tiny plants of varied form and starry blossom? But, unfortunately, the climate is not an alpine climate, and the lowland grasses easily and rapidly dominate most of the plants which one endeavours to introduce among them. The best chance of success, one would say, lies among such aggressive and persistent carpeters as the smaller Cotulas and Acænas, which are lowland settlers of a warlike disposition; yet the grass has beaten them out every time. But an unexpected plant is now proving its capacity for meeting the grass on equal terms. It is that pretty little ramping *Veronica filiformis*, with roundish-cordate fresh green hairy leaves and a wealth of very pale blue flowers in spring, which most people grow, but for which few seem to have a name. It is spreading rapidly through the grass, and does not seem to mind the lawn-mower a bit, and next spring will make a rather pretty feature, I fancy.

THE LONG-SUFFERING PLANT.

The difference in adaptability of plants to their surroundings is very interesting, and quite beyond the power of botanists to explain. We may carve a plant to pieces and examine every portion under the microscope without getting a hint as to whether it can stand frost or great heat. A scarcity or excess of water in a plant's natural habitat more often leaves its impress upon the plant's body; but by no means always. The Marsh Fern has grown for years with me mixed with *Anthyllis montana.* Looking at them, how can one tell that the former naturally grows in swamps, where it is often under water half the year, while the other haunts dry rocks exposed to the hot sun of southern Europe? *Sedum multiceps* and *Ephedra altissima,* from the semi-deserts of northern Africa jostle with the Iceland Poppy and Bear-berry, whose headquarters are within the Arctic. To the first two our country must be a horribly cold, wet place; to the latter pair a veritable hothouse. Yet they all jog along quite comfortably.

The truth seems to be that when free competition is eliminated the strict geographical limits which often define a plant's natural growth vanish, and it is able to show that it can live under much more varied conditions than would appear from its natural range. Fortunate for gardeners that it is so, and that most plants will so cheerfully accept anything in reason in the way of accommodation. But there are notorious exceptions. What about that disastrous beauty, *Eritrichium nanum*? Who can grow *Diapensia lapponica*? And think of all the love wasted in vain on *Ranunculus glacialis* and *Pyxidanthera barbulata*, and *Saxifraga florulenta*, and the species of Hudsonia. These are not adaptable; some want of theirs we do not understand and fail to supply (if it is possible to supply it in a garden) in spite of all experience.

But since the requirements of plants are so mysterious, it is well to experiment to some extent with many of them. A plant may be doing well enough with us, but be capable of doing much better under slightly different conditions. I find it well worth while, when I get a new plant, to take off any piece that will come easily, or at least a few cuttings, and put these in where conditions of soil and light and moisture are different. Then one sees which does best, and gets a useful hint. Often a cutting has grown where the plant has died.

CONTINENTS ADRIFT.

SOME vast amount of years ago, when a travesty of geography (in the form of lists of towns, rivers, and natural products) was being injected into one's youthful brain, who does not remember puzzling over the queer shapes of continents and seas, and wondering what it all meant? And, indeed, if one has not lost with accumulating years the divine gift of curiosity, who can look at a map of the world without wondering still? The subject is a fascinating one; it has long occupied the attention of geologists and geophysicists. There was the Lyellian idea of alternating ups and downs of the land and sea areas, like the two ends of a see-saw—

> " There where the long street roars hath been
> The stillness of the central sea."

Later on, we heard a great deal about the permanence of the ocean-basins : they had been from the beginning and would be for evermore. But in direct opposition to this, the biologists, convinced by the striking similarity of the animals and plants inhabiting lands on opposite sides of the oceans that these lands must have been connected in former times, began to fill up the oceans with land-bridges or " bridging-continents," to provide the necessary terrestrial continuity (though what became of all the water under these circumstances was not made clear).

Then in 1915 Alfred Wegener, Professor of Geophysics at the University of Graz, published a book[1] in which remarkable and daring speculations on this subject were put forward, logically worked out on evidence drawn from very varied sources. On account of the war, Wegener's hypothesis received rather tardy attention, but during the last few years it has been much debated among scientific men. The appearance of an English edition[2] has now placed within reach of all readers in these countries a remarkable work; whether its main thesis eventually stands or falls, it has exercised upon the study of geography and geophysics a most stimulating influence, and has caused geologists and biologists to examine their store of accumulated facts from a new angle.

Briefly stated, Wegener's contention is that the continents are not necessarily fixed in their positions, but float upon a heavier lower layer of the earth's crust, and are capable of drifting about, very much as ice-floes drift in water; and further, that the continents have attained their present shapes and positions by the breaking up of a single great land-mass which existed some millions of years ago.

This may seem very fantastic and sensational; but a large body of evidence can be adduced to bring the mechanism of it at least within the limits of possibility, and, without question, its application explains many puzzling features of the Earth's surface, and

1 Die Entstehung der Kontinente und Ozeane. Braunschweig, 1915.

2 A. Wegener: The Origin of Continents and Oceans. Translated from the third German edition by J. G. A. Skerl. Methuen. 1924.

offers a solution of some problems which have hitherto remained insoluble.

In order to understand the basis of Wegener's work it is necessary to recall certain conclusions to which research has led regarding the surface and the surface layers of the Earth. The mapping of the continents has shown that in spite of an obvious diversity of level—mountain ranges and so on— the elevation above the sea (which forms a convenient datum) of the great bulk of the land areas lies between narrow limits, and averages about 2,300 feet. More recent work has shown for the oceanic areas also a prevailing depth, which lies at about 2,100 fathoms. A model to illustrate these facts could be made by sketching out on an orange the continents and oceans, and then removing the rind over the oceanic areas. The orange parts would then represent—with a great exaggeration of the vertical scale—the raised land areas and the white portions would represent the ocean beds. (Mountain ranges are in reality an insignificant feature of the Earth's surface. Everest upon our orange would be but a microscopic grain of dust). The oceans themselves do not affect the argument; a lot of water was left lying on the surface of the earth when it originally cooled, and this has naturally collected in the lowest areas. Another fact, abundantly proved, is that these land areas are lighter than the deep-buried layers on which they rest. And, furthermore, although both upper and lower layers are pliable, the lower layer is the more so. An effect of this is that where the upper layer becomes thicker, as at a mountain range, it sinks into the lower one until the difference of weight is compensated, and vice-versa where the upper crust is thinner. Just as if we had a flexible floating raft: if one portion of the raft were loaded, that portion would sink deeper into the water until equilibrium was restored. Wegener believes that the upper layer forming the lands, and the areas occupied by seas of inconsiderable depth or " continental shelves " which are associated with them, represent an outer light shell—a kind of scum—floating on a heavier lower layer, which is exposed (save for the overlying water) in the ocean beds, and is buried under the land areas. The upper layer—possibly once continuous, as the lower one is—is now broken up into continents, and in many places crushed together into mountain-ranges. The surface of the lower layer, lying evenly where the pressure is even, as under the oceans, is depressed under the land areas by their superincumbent weight. A close analogy may be found in the behaviour of ice-flows and icebergs, and the water in which they float.

But now we come to the sensational part of the business. Our author puts forward a mass of evidence in favour of the contention that these floating continents are not anchored in their places, but are drifting, and have drifted far from their former positions. (There are powerful agencies which affect the Earth's surface at the present time, such as its rotation, and the pull of the sun and moon, which might well cause a floating continent to move). He postulates a former single great land mass, which has broken up. A long north-and-south rift has allowed America to drift away westward; the Antarctic continent has moved south; Australia has also drifted off. India, formerly lying alongside South Africa, has been telescoped northward into the main mass of Asia, crumpling up the land into the Himalayas. Figures in his book show very clearly these supposed movements, which he believes to have commenced in what geologists call Jurassic times, and very possibly to be still in progress—there is some evidence, as yet not very satisfactory, that Greenland is moving westward. Now, if a page of this book had been torn across, and the two parts were brought together again, the fitting in of the torn margins, and the continuity of the lines of print, would be accepted by anyone as proof that the page had once formed a continuous sheet. Wegener applies this test to the land on either side of the Atlantic Ocean. He points out that not only does the shoreline of the two Americas fit surprisingly the shoreline of Europe and Africa, but that many of the broad geological features on either side, such as east-and-west foldings of the crust and outcrops of rock, coincide exactly and become continuous. Again, if a moving continent had forced its way through the heavy mass on which it rests, we might look for some of the phenomena which are usually associated with such movements, as when a mass of clay is pushed along the ground. We might expect a crumpling up of the front of the mass, a dropping off behind of detached pieces, a sagging back of the wings. In the Americas all these features

are present—the great Andean mountain chain
stretching the whole length of the continent; the
numerous detached islands on the eastern side
—none on the western; the eastward bend at Cape
Horn. And he applies these and other tests to
different parts of the Earth's surface with equal skill.

Of many other arguments marshalled by our
Austrian professor, only one can be mentioned. It
is well known that in the remote times defined by
geologists as Permo-Carboniferous, there was a
period of great cold comparable to that quite recent
Ice Age, the wreckage of which is still strewn everywhere over our own island. A widespread glaciation
like this can be brought about only by an extension
of the Polar ice-cap, whether the Pole remains in its
present location or moves to some new position.
But so scattered are the areas which lay under ice
during this Permo-Carboniferous glaciation (South
America, South Africa, India, Australia) that no
position of the Pole can be postulated which will
not involve in the glaciation a vast and quite impossible area of the Earth's surface. No plausible
explanation of this puzzle has ever been put
forward till Wegener reconstructed his " Pangaea "
or single continent, on which the glaciated areas lie
conveniently together so that a movement of the
South Pole (a quite conceivable thing) might bring
them all within the radius of an ice-cap of reasonable dimensions.

Much more might be written on these brilliant and
daring speculations, but enough has been said to
indicate the lines of argument used and the conclu-

sions reached. To the biologist, the " Theory of the Displacement of Continents " (to give it its official title) especially appeals. Forced by the close relationships in both past and present times, of the animals and plants of distant parts of the world, he was compelled either to endow them with powers of dispersal of a quite improbable degree, or to invoke, amid clamorous protests from the geologists, numerous and gigantic land-bridges—to " make continents as easily as a cook does pancakes," as Darwin expressed it—in order to lead his Israelites into the promised lands. Wegener's suggestions render such vast architectural efforts unnecessary, and offer a solution of many biological puzzles.

It may be asked—But why did these movements only begin in times which are, geologically speaking, comparatively recent? The fossil evidence which supports the idea of a former combination of existing land surfaces also points to a long life for this super-continent prior to its break-up. I do not think that Wegener deals with this point, but more recently Joly has put forward a striking explanation. He reminds us that the heat generated in the interior of the earth by the breaking-down of radio-active substances is, in all probability, greater than the heat lost by radiation from the surface, so that our Earth, instead of getting colder, is actually getting hotter. (Alas! for another of our early beliefs—the cooling globe, the shrunken apple!) When this heating-up reaches a certain point, the layer in which the continents are embedded, till then sufficiently rigid to hold the land-masses in place, will soften, he suggests, till the blocks of "land" are free to move under the tidal and other forces which act upon them. The land-masses will also be softened by the intense heat below them, and will lose their cohesion. Rifts will appear, there will be great volcanic outbursts, earthquakes, and all sorts of terrestrial fireworks, lasting until the accumulated energy has been dissipated, when the rocks will again harden up, the continents will be once more frozen into whatever positions they may have drifted to, and the whole process will begin again. Now, the known history of the Earth, as unravelled by geologists, shows three periods, separated by many millions of years, of exceptional and catastrophic volcanic activity, and the intervals of time between these periods can be approximately estimated. On the other hand, calculations based on the estimated radium content of the rocks, and the rate of accumulation of heat due to its breaking down, point to lengths of time between these periodic outbursts of approximately similar amount. This coincidence lends added weight to the geological evidence, tends to support the idea of long-separated cataclysms, and may account for the lengthy period of quiescence on the Pangaean continent prior to its destruction.

Wegener's theory has been vigorously assailed, in whole or in part. This was to be expected, for the subject bristles with difficulties, and much is yet unexplored. But whether it stands the test of time, or whether, under the pressure of fresh observation and discovery, it eventually "goes west" (as it claims that America has done), the Theory of the Displacement of Continents marks a forward step in the knowledge of our planet, and one whose influence will long be felt in that Every Man's Land where geologists, geographers, physicists, chemists, and biologists meet together for the common study of our mother Earth.

THE ROAD TO RILO.

FROM Sofia you may reach the great Rilo Monastery, lying forty miles to the southward, by alternative routes. You can go by train, a long day's journey, starting away westward through the gorge between the 7,000-foot Vitosche and its smaller neighbour Ljulin; then meandering for hours on a narrow gauge line up hill and down dale through maize and vines and orchards. At last you strike the yellow Struma, and descending its parching sandy valley you outflank the Rilo Mountains and, slipping in behind them, you turn back and crawl up a long glen. Deeper and deeper into the forest-clad hills you go, till at 4,000 feet the panting engine stops with a jerk and you see the tall monastery buildings on the other side of a roaring stream, surrounded on every side by primeval forest stretching far up steep mountain sides. Or preferably you go direct by motor and horse: south from Sofia across the plain and up twenty miles of mountain gorge, and out into the plain again to dusty Samakov. If you are wise you will not stay there, but push on and up to Tchamkouri, beloved of the Sofia people, with its scattered villas embowered in pine forests and its fresh mountain air, so welcome after the baking motor roads, all ruts and dust. Thither we came on an August Sunday, to find friends awaiting us and a warm Bulgarian welcome, and a delicious cool wind coming down from the snow-flecked

summits.   We lingered one day in order to scale
Musallah (" the Seat of God ") the highest point in
south-eastern Europe—riding up through the fragrant pine-woods, through miles of alpine pasture gay
with unfamiliar flowers, then on foot past dark tarns,
marshy places full of the rare and lovely *Primula
deorum*—well called " of the Gods "—and rocks
decked with great woolly tufts of the equally rare
Geum bulgaricum; and finally up across screes and
snow-fields to the windy summit.

Early next morning ponies were waiting under
the shade of the pines, and we started on the finest
and most adventurous ride that we have had, across
the almost trackless main ridge of Rilo.   On the
Canaries we had ridden among great precipices and
over lofty hills, but there was mostly a well-marked
track.   It was different here.   You remember how
in the " Magic Flute " the hero and heroine walk
sedately through ordeals of fire and water and
thunder, to the accompaniment of Mozart's lovely
music.   Before the day was over we felt rather like
them, but not nearly so placid, in spite of the best
of all music—the thunder of the waterfalls, the sigh-
ing of the wind in the clinging pines, and the
echoing cry of the eagles.   First there was short
slippery grass on a steep sun-baked slope, where two
of our party came to grief, one getting a heavy fall
into a gully.   Then rushing torrents had to be
crossed, full of great boulders and deep holes, where
our sure-footed little beasts proved their cleverness.
Worse than this was a steeply sloping scree of
angular blocks, about as large as travelling trunks,

piled in wild confusion, their upper faces polished as smooth as glass by the passage of horses and mules during centuries. Across this our ponies staggered and skidded, but not one of them came down. And high up, dense low groves of Mountain Pine overhung the upper side of the track, and wiry branches scooped one clean out of the saddle if one was not alert in lying flat on the pony's back. A sporting experience for fair weather riders like us.

But the beauty and interest of that long day would have compensated for far more adventurous happenings. First along the foot-hills; then through the gates of a magnificent gorge, with towering cliffs hung with many plants which in our gardens rank as great treasures. On for miles through rock and forest, our ponies climbing and stumbling and wading, while our horse-boys scoured the woods for the wild strawberries which grew everywhere. Then came the midday halt on a flat bit of natural meadow, with a great fire to warm us—for we were getting well up now—and smoked meat and cheese of sheep's milk and roasted paprika and dried fish, followed by a long stretch to take away stiffness. Then on and up over much rougher ground, floundering and scrambling through boulders and bushes and rushing waters, till at length we saw in front the great stretches of alpine meadow and Mountain Pine and snow that extend over the higher grounds. We crossed the pass at 7,000 feet, and looked down into a glorious valley, its sides crowned with great crags, its bottom embosoming a small lake, beyond which miles of forest faded into a purple haze. The descent was much too steep and rough for riding, and we walked for hours through sheets of alpine flowers, past the lake and the huge moraine which dams it, and on through forests of the largest trees we had ever seen—conifers and beeches—till a final zig-zag descent of a thousand feet down the track of an avalanche brought us to the first signs of human activity. Dusk fell, and the mystery of the woods deepened, the great grey trunks towering like columns into the darkness of the canopy two hundred feet above. At length a light, and suddenly we were among a crowd of people around booths whose flickering flares lighted up dimly the towering mass of the monastery walls. Through a sounding archway we went, its sides covered with mural paintings dimly seen, and halted in the courtyard beyond. A large irregular quadrangle of four-storey buildings, each storey with a gaily-painted broad verandah; in the middle a Byzantine church with a square medieval tower. Flickering lamps here and there; torches moving about; everywhere the pleasant sound of running water and the hum and rustle of a multitude of people. After a little delay we were led to the rooms reserved for us, which were those occupied by the bishop when he visits the monastery—a kitchen, dining-room, and a great sitting-room, with beds and sleeping shelves, all covered like the floor with handsome rugs, the gifts of pious pilgrims.

Next morning the daylight shows us more of the monastery, a very hive of human life, for here are a thousand monks and often a thousand pilgrims.

The monks are striking figures—black coats down
to the ankles, black hats like top-hats upside down,
bushy black beards and hair—for the use of scissors
or razors is forbidden.   Their sombreness sets off
the gay national costumes of the country folk, and
makes the smart clothes of pilgrims from the towns
look incongruous.   In each corner of the courtyard plentiful ice-cold water from the hills plunges
into a stone trough.   Here all washing is done—
whether personal or household—and there is much
gossip and laughter.   Upstairs it is lively too, for the
pilgrims do their own cooking—save bloated aristocrats like ourselves, for word has got about that we
are friends of the King's, and we have a servant-
monk to wait on us.   The church in the courtyard
is remarkable, for every inch of its walls, inside and
out, is covered with religious paintings in stiff medieval style.   Inside are many bible history subjects,
and Creations and Last Judgments. Outside the art-
ists have specialised in demonology, and if there is
one devil depicted there, there are twenty thousand,
engaged in every sort of devilry that infernal ingenuity could suggest.   A monk appears bearing in one
hand a long piece of wood, and in the other a mallet.
He walks slowly three times round the church,
striking the mallet against the wood and producing a
loud semi-musical sound—tap, tap, tap-tap-tap-tap—
getting quicker and quicker to a climax and then
beginning again.   This is a summons to public wor-
ship, a relic of Turkish rule, when Christian bells
were prohibited. We pay a visit of ceremony to the
abbot, and sign the visitors' book, in which we

see many well-known names—English cabinet ministers, famous travellers, foreign potentates, and what not. But most of our time is spent in the glorious forests which rise on all sides for a couple of thousand feet above the monastery, and on the alpine meadows and precipices that climb thence to eight thousand feet. Here wild nature reigns undisturbed: bears and wolves, wild boars and a score of different kinds of snakes, live at ease; and everywhere extends a fascinating alpine flora—recalling strongly that of Switzerland, but different in almost every species, and displaying at each turn some of the greatest treasures of our rock gardens. It is a difficult choice for the lover of nature: Switzerland with its innumerable facilities—hotels, railways, roads, paths penetrating everywhere, each stream exploited for electric power and each forest for its timber—everything easy, everything clean, everything mapped out—or the Rilo mountains, still untouched by man; in consequence no hotels (many of the substitutes might crawl bodily away, so astonishing is the number and variety of their insect inhabitants), no roads save on the lower grounds, no electric wires, scarcely a house or a track anywhere: only the solemn glory of the virgin forests, and of the unscaled sun-kissed crags.

SNAKES IN ICELAND.

For the enlightenment of those unfortunates who have not been led to interest themselves in natural history, it may be well to expound the zoological chestnut which is enshrined in the title that impends over this brief discourse. In the year 1752 Niels Horrebow published his *Tilforladelige Efterret-ningger om Island*. For the sake of the present writer as much as of the reader, I shall quote from the English translation, which was published in 1758 under the title, *The Natural History of Iceland*. The seventy-second chapter of the book reads as follows:—

" Chap. lxxii. *Concerning Snakes.*

No snakes of any kind are to be met with throughout the whole island."

That is all. There is nothing more to be said, save that for the sake of the story it is better to leave our Danish author there, since further enquiry shows that he had an ulterior reason for being so categorical, and further, that he was not, as a matter of fact, so categorical as his English translator would lead us to suppose.

It may be of interest to consider what are the animals and plants which we might expect to find in our own country, but which in Ireland, like the Icelandic reptiles, are conspicuous only by their absence. Of snakes themselves it is of course, hardly necessary to speak. We know all about their *débacle*.

> "He gave the snakes and toads a twist,
> And banished them for ever."

And the Saint's excommunicatory thunder reverberates yet—the curse is still O.K.—for when traitorous persons, plotting to reduce our country to the reptilian level of England, have turned loose in Ireland Ringed Snakes and so on, they have all instantly perished—the snakes, that is, and for all I know the traitors also. Zoologists are at pains to point out that this is the common fate of attempts to introduce exotic animals into any fresh area; but we know better—St. Patrick understood his business. In some respects, however, he was just a trifle careless, for he overlooked the little Natterjack Toad down in Kerry; and we have also the Common Frog (long believed to have been introduced since Patrick's time, but now known on fossil evidence to have long antedated him), and one kind of lizard and one kind of newt.

But the absences from Ireland as compared with England are very interesting, and well worthy of our consideration. Among the reptiles, for instance, the Ringed Snake, Viper, and Slow-Worm are all common across the Channel, the latter two extending to the North of Scotland; yet none of them is here. Of amphibians, the Great Crested Newt and Common Toad are missing, although spread throughout Great Britain. Among the mammals, quite a number of British species, including some of the most characteristic denizens of the English countryside, are unknown over here—the Weasel (our Irish "weasel" is really the Stoat, an allied but distinct animal), the Mole, the Common Hare (our species being the Mountain Hare, a different creature), the Wild Cat, the Pole-cat, and several voles or "water-rats," mice, shrew-mice, and bats. Against this, Ireland has not a single distinct species among the higher animals which is not also found across the Channel. It is true that the Irish Stoat, for instance, is by specialists separated from the English form, but the differences are really very slight.

Now, this is a very long list of Irish absentees, when we think how close the two islands lie to each other, and how generally similar in climate, soil, and so on, Down, Dublin, and Wexford are to Galloway, Lancashire, and Cardigan. It suggests that the intervening strip of water is a feature of much significance. But before going further it will be well to enquire whether our Irish wild-flowers have the same tale to tell. Comparison of the British and Irish floras shows that they have. Many plants which are common on the eastern side of the Irish Sea, and which display their adaptability to differences of climate by extending from the Land's End and Kent to the Tweed or further, are, nevertheless, absent from Ireland; for instance, the Common Rock-Rose, the White Byrony, the Black Byrony, the Wayfaring-Tree, and a number of others. In this case the converse does not hold good, for Ireland possesses a number of higher plants, and very interesting ones, too, which are absent from Great Britain: but that, the most fascinating chapter of Irish botany, needs a sermon to itself. The fact remains that on crossing the Irish Sea from Holyhead to Dun Laoghaire we lose a greater number of our higher animals and plants in the sixty miles than on the two hundred and fifty miles from London to Holyhead. Did these forms of life never reach Ireland, or have they got across and subsequently died out? The evidence is all in favour of the former view, for their remains have never been found in Ireland, nor does any trace or tradition exist to tell us of their sojourn here in either prehistoric or historic times. It is quite conceivable that such a thing might have happened. Exceptional drought or heat or cold often kills out an animal or plant in a particular area, and if that area is isolated by water so that the species cannot easily re-immigrate from neighbouring places, it may vanish permanently. But in this particular case it would appear that the animals and plants in question never were here. If we study the fauna and flora of the two sides of the North Sea and English Channel we shall find a similar contrast, greater than can be explained by the more insular climate of Great Britain. The group of islands of which Ireland forms one lies on a wide shelf extending out from the continental coast, very thinly covered with water as compared with the ocean depths that lie to the westward of it. The relative level of land and sea is not fixed, but is, and has always been, in a state of change. On many occasions in past geological times a rise of the land-level has caused the sea to recede from off this shelf, connecting the higher parts, such as at present form Great Britain and Ireland, with the Continent. During these periods plants and animals could migrate by land into our own area, and the great waves of migration which swept across Europe from the large land-masses to the eastward spent themselves only when they reached an ancient coast-line lying west of the present Ireland. But many of the animals and plants which now people Europe are comparatively recent arrivals there, and ere these reached the West, the final separation of our islands had taken place. First the Irish connection broke down, so that organisms which were able still to invade Great Britain from the Continent were held up on the shores of the newly-formed Irish Sea—the Mole, Polecat, Adder, Common Toad, Rock-Rose, Bryony, and so on, already referred to. A subsequent depression gave rise to the Straits of Dover, and cut off further European migration into England. That both animals and plants sometimes leap these barriers, and by the agency of currents or wind or flying birds effect an entry into our countries is beyond question, and, of course, flying creatures are well equipped for this purpose. But even with the latter, trans-marine migration is curiously rare, and our little strip of sea remains zoologically and botanically, as it has always been politically and socially, a very real boundary, not to be eliminated by fast mail steamers or telegraph cables, aeroplanes or wireless receivers.

EAST WIND.

This morning the wind is in the east, and I have an early start to make. It may be an effect of that unhappy conjunction of circumstances, or it may be that I have got out at the wrong side of the bed; but for whatever reason, things seem less cheerful than usual. My window looks northward across the square, ghostly in the January dawn. Athwart the sky from right to left, stretches a broad black bar of filthy smoke. It is there on every east wind day, pouring from the twin chimneys of the electrical power station. It rolls away towards the Phœnix Park, cutting the sky in twain as the river does the city—a sooty Sword of Damocles brooding over Dublin. When the breeze is southerly, my window gazes on a similar outrage over to the left—a high chimney pouring forth an incredibly copious cloud which rains soot over the uncomplaining collections in the National Museum. I think of the impassioned appeals of the City Commissioners for aesthetic amenities in our beloved Dublin, and wonder, as I button a refractory collar, how that stoical triumvirate or the Government or even the amorphous inarticulate public can continue either to countenance or to endure such an affront on the decent cleanliness of our city. (But then, as I have suggested, the east wind is in my bones this morning, and everything is viewed with a jaundiced eye).

Now a sound as of distant bombardment echoes

menacingly through the silent streets; again it
comes, nearer, clearer, deadlier than before—the city
Cleansing Department is awake and at work—is up
and at 'em. How the ash-bins withstand the
onslaughts of these heroic refuse-fighters is one of
the many mysteries that Dublin offers to the
romantic-minded. And the volume of defiant noise
that an adept can extract from an ash-bin is indeed
astonishing. The value of the service that these
devoted men perform in rousing the sleeping city
to another day's toil does not meet with the approba-
tion which it merits. Three days a week, punctually
at seven of the clock, their tocsin sounds, and rest
becomes impossible. Fitzwilliam Square on a frosty
morning can vie with Sandy Row on the glorious
Twelfth.

The streets are wet and shining as I hurry to catch
an early train. The ash-bins, despoiled, lidless,
battered, but unconquered, stretch in wavering
perspective along the footpath; one thinks of the thin
red line at Waterloo, of the dauntless burghers of
Leyden, of the Turks in the Plevna trenches. The
enemy has retired in good order, but without the
whole of the spoils. Prior to his onslaught, children
and hungry dogs have been at work. The much-
enduring sarcophagi have been ransacked for cinders
and bones and bread, as testified by the spilt rubbish,
and by the ghostly sheets of paper that blow about
the street. Dirty newspapers and empty tins!
Were it not that (Heaven be praised!) they perish
soon, this age would be known to archæologists of
the next millennium as a dreadful epoch, a relapse

into barbarity, characterized by a universal dominance of tins and paper, just as the Bronze Age in Ireland is now famed for its wealth of golden torcs and lunulae.   Tins, admittedly, do not lend themselves readily to immediate destruction; but as for paper, those wretches who in the country scatter it where they picnic, or in town put it into ash-bins, instead of setting a match to it as nature intended, ought to be clothed in an *Independent* and put in the stocks at the foot of Sir John Gray's statue. (Decidedly I am out of sorts this morning).

Along the canal, the misty morning light is not unpleasing.   The stately rows of elms, which received such savage mutilation some years ago, are again shapely.   Nature, that patient mother, has healed their wounds, and they form once more a lovely avenue.   Underneath, the canal stretches, grass-fringed, silver-grey, its only argosies two dead dogs and more paper.   Through a gloomy cavern with an echoing roof of iron and an ammoniacal atmosphere I pass, like a soul in purgatory, to the most depressing railway terminus the world knows. It feels its shame, and shrinking back from the street, hides its infirmities behind tall screens of wood.   To north, west, and south they rise like battlements, many yards in height, with lofty outworks on the further side of Hatch Street and Harcourt Road, and strong bridgeheads along the canal, menacing Ranelagh and Rathmines.   And from these Wooden Walls of Ireland, whiskies, underclothing, cinemas, coal, motor-cars, mustard and music-halls, cod-liver oil and corsets, oxo, rinso, bisto, lasto, and what-not-o, shriek for recognition from an apathetic public. The clashing colours, the bad drawing, the hideousness of the whole medley might freeze the blood of the most hardy; so withering a barrage of arrow-fire from these ancient defences, deadly as that of Senlac, might well send the last would-be passenger staggering back with his suit-case towards Stephen's Green, though clad in triple steel. But no; Dublin passes by unscathed, in maiden meditation, fancy free.

The station steps are deserted save for a croaking newsboy. The single melancholy platform is empty except for a truckload of newspapers and some milk-cans. I discover that I have arrived half-an-hour too early. The rain has come down again, driving gustily below grey hurrying cloud. It is darker than ever, and the station is like a vault. Did Charon's passengers travel by rail instead of boat, one might expect to see him standing here, sad-eyed, waiting. I pace the patched asphalt, alone and thinking of death.

* * * * *

In the afternoon, a visit to Sir Patrick Dun's Hospital. Such communion with the still sad music of humanity has a chastening influence, but does not tend to raise drooping spirits. The rain has stopped, and in Holles Street scores of children are playing in the gutter. I pass to Merrion Square, its acres of grass and shrubs neglected and empty, and wonder what is out of joint with the times, that the children should play in the mud among the motor-cars instead of in that healthful expanse. It gives a

K

feeling of satisfaction to note that the unpainted railing, the grim barrier that shuts off the promised land, is rotting through at the base; some day it will fall, and perhaps (but how much *perhaps*!) the children will come into their own.

On the chilly footpath, in the shelter of the bushes, a small cat, a half-grown Persian, is one of the few moving things. It accosts each passer-by in turn, tail erect and little red mouth wide open, craving a kind word; and it is seldom repulsed. Will that rough, burly, red-faced man, who looks like a drover from the midlands, respond to its appeal? Yes, he too stoops and strokes its head, while the little creature rubs purring against his muddy gaiters. Most mysterious, this love and trustfulness of dogs and cats for us blundering humans; perhaps they feel sorry for us, befogged sojourners, like themselves, in " the Prison men call Life," but with such infinite capacity for good, and so sorry a record of good accomplished. A lanky Alsatian comes loping along, and the cat slips quietly through the railings, and sits watching quizzically its hostile demonstrations—some use for the railings after all!

About Baggot Street new petrol pumps, scarlet and yellow, have sprung up in the night, like poisonous fungi. It is curious that the motor-car, which in itself is mostly (save for its murderous propensities) an inoffensive and sometimes even graceful feature of our modern traffic, should when stationary induce such unmitigated ugliness—stark concrete garages, which might drive a jerry-builder to suicide, and glaring robot-like monstrosities extruding on our quiet-toned streets their ungainly forms and vulgar garishness.

I run the gauntlet of Merrion Row with its population of screeching newsboys, shivering singers (save the mark!) and pathetic cripples, and gaining the comparative calm of Dawson Street, observe with concern that the high-perched time-piece which keeps watch over the Provost's garden indicates five minutes past four, for I am due at " The Bridge" at four o'clock. Reassurance comes on reaching Grafton Street, where two dials proclaim that it still wants a minute of the hour. But Trinity College thinks differently, and opines that it is three minutes past. The *Irish Times* agrees with it (as it does occasionally) but the Ballast Office (strange name for the home of the Port and Docks Board) announces that full three further minutes of eternity have still to be enacted. Are these perplexing discrepancies due to a lofty disregard on the part of the clock-keepers for mere minutes, or has a whiff of Einsteinian relativity escaped from the ancient home of the higher mathematics that fronts College Green; or do they nod, those earthly godfathers of heaven's lights who give a name to every fixèd star, and ordain the time of day for us? Poor Dubliner, who knows not what to believe since he sees nothing clear, and dares stamp nothing false where he finds nothing sure. How much more simple is life in Belfast, where one has but to believe in William of Orange and the Albert Memorial, and all the intricacies and perplexities of this bourn of time and place vanish away.

The quays, with their muddy square setts, are noisy and dirty as usual, and in the dimming light the waiting 'buses are dull blobs of blue and yellow and red against the dull buildings. The Liffey is at lowest ebb, and its subaqueous population of forsaken buckets and weedy stones increases as I go rattling and banging up-stream on a wet tram-top. I return to the mud at Grattan Bridge, feeling I am rapidly approaching that stage of dejection which drives the strong-minded to a public-house, when from low down in the western sky there comes a gleam of yellow light, rapidly broadening and brightening. And then suddenly five great swans appear, flying down the centre of the river. In perfect formation, long necks outstretched, broad wings beating in unison, they sweep by majestically, a vision of pure beauty, gleaming plumage all snowy against the old houses opposite. While I still watch their receding forms fading into the smoky mist, a low red sun bursts out from underneath the last bank of cloud. It floods down the river; the long vista of dull houses lights up in a dozen lovely shades through a faint pink haze; the spires and towers behind stand up transfigured; the dirty water turns to gold and silver. One gazes at a dream city, beautiful beyond belief. And while I stand, a breath of softer air, bringing with it hope and a lifting of the spirit, comes from the west: the wind has changed.

A STUDY IN DIMENSION.

PHYSICAL science, advancing at an extraordinary rate during the last half century, tends more and more to clothe itself in a special nomenclature. This is a natural result of the discovery or elucidation of phenomena unknown to or unexplained by previous generations, necessitating the employment of fresh terms. The new terminology tends towards conciseness and precision of expression among men of science, but renders it increasingly difficult for the layman who attempts to probe into modern mysteries. What the reader encounters when he adventures into the results of present-day research is still English so far as construction and grammar are concerned, but, even apart from mathematical formulæ, the key-words are mostly unfamiliar. One flounders helplessly among protons, millecuries, isotopes, angströms, gamma rays, ohms, quanta, ergs, and so on. Fortunately some of our leaders in science realise the difficulties which confront the non-scientific reader in the face of new conceptions and new words, and stoop to help us in our need. In a recent fascinating volume,* Sir James Jeans sets himself the formidable task of demonstrating to the ordinary man the Universe itself according to modern views. He succeeds so well that the book is being extensively read by those who desire some knowledge of the vast and of the minute

* *The Universe Around Us.* Cambridge University Press. 1929.

—of what is outside of this infinitesimally small scrap of matter on which we carry on the business of life and death, which we call the Earth, as well as of the complicated structure of every one of the grains of dust out of which the Earth is built up.

This question of scientific language is not the only or the worst stumbling-block in the way of him who would seek to probe the physical mysteries which surround us. More difficult is it to produce a mental picture of the dimensions with which we have to deal if we would acquire any conception of natural phenomena, from their minutest to their grandest manifestations—say from atoms to stellar galaxies (though neither an atom nor a galaxy comes anywhere near the ultimate limit on the scale of either actual smallness or actual bigness). This question of dimension is worthy of a few minutes' consideration.

Even if we take a range of size running from one million millionth to one million millions—which is far within the limits with which the astro-physicist has to deal—what do these words mean to us? Even a single beggarly million: the term produces no clear impression on the mind. To suggest the meaning of a million it is usual to translate it into some formula like this:—if a clerk in the Paymaster-General's office set himself to check a million coins, counting at the rate of one per second for ordinary working hours, he would not put the final tick on his return till the end of two months.

The Universe, vast beyond belief, and everything within it, is made up of atoms, small beyond realisation; and the nature and properties of the atom dominate every phenomenon to be found in the Universe. Our author is therefore at pains to instruct us as to the modern conception of the atom —the "mighty atom" in very truth. And it is bewildering to find that this infinitesimal unit, out of which the hardest of solids and the most ethereal of gases are alike made up, is not a simple or inert body, but highly complicated, its parts widely separated, and full of rapid motion. Indeed the only phenomenon in nature of which we have any clear conception (or think we have), to which we may liken the structure of the atom, is the Solar System itself. The atom, like the Solar System, has a central sun, the nucleus, and around this its remaining constituents, the electrons, it may be one or it may be up to close on a hundred of them, whirl in a complex of elliptical orbits. So small are the constituent particles in relation to their distance apart that the simile of the Solar System is quite reasonable; yet so minute is the whole intricate structure that if you were to enlarge an atom to the size of a cricket ball in order to get a good look at it, you would have to enlarge your cricket ball to the size of the Earth in order to preserve the proportion between the two.

This view of the nature of the atom has passed far beyond the region of speculation: short of actually seeing atoms—which we need never hope to do—we can ask no further proof of their constitution than what modern physics now gives; yet how difficult is it for us to conceive that we ourselves and everything we behold—flesh, clothes, rainbows and rail-way trains, the wind that blows, the great Globe itself—are nothing but agglomerated masses of these impossibly tenuous and ridiculously minute whirli-gigs.

So much for the lower end of our scale of dimen-sions in nature. Multiply up your atom by so many billion billion billion billions (whatever that may mean) and you produce a body which we imagine we can better envisage—namely, a star, the visible unit of which the Universe is mainly composed. But does the fact that we can gaze at these points of light set in a blue-black sky, and study one of them, our Sun, at the quite reasonable distance of ninety-three millions of miles, make it in any degree easier for us to envisage either their size, their distribution, or the amazing conditions prevailing upon them—these " fixed stars," which are all tearing along at rates compared to which an express train is merely stationary, and which, with lives of millions of millions of years, are nevertheless burning them-selves up at the rate of millions of tons a second? Our own Sun is a very average star—a blazing mass some two thousand million million million million tons in weight, and with a temperature even at its surface compared to which the difference between boiling water and ice is merely negligible. It is rather larger, brighter, and hotter than the average, but not markedly so. The stars do not vary excessively in regard to size, but in some other respects there are startling differences among them. For instance, some are enormously hotter than the

average—were the star *S* Doradus to replace our
Sun, the temperature at the Earth's surface would
jump to 7,000 degrees centigrade, which would cause
the mountains to melt and the oceans to explode,
and the whole Earth to vanish in a cloud of vapour.
Some are extraordinarily dense; in van Maanen's star
ten tons of matter are squeezed into each cubic inch;
others are amazingly tenuous. And so on: sensational
comparisons like these are the mainstay of every
popular book on descriptive astronomy. Jeans'
work gives a very clear account of the nature of the
evidence on which such statements are based; of
the observations by which stars are weighed,
measured, their materials analysed, and their distances and motions determined. Then there are
double stars which whizz eternally round each other
like butterflies playing; variable stars, which regu-
larly or irregularly blaze up furiously and die down
again; star-groups, like the Pleiades and the Plough,
which sail through space in company, like flocks of
birds; queer half-made stars, and vast clouds of star-
dust which have not yet condensed; but the great
majority of stars are suns like our own.

And do these stars which we watch at night
stretch on through space for ever and ever? By no
means. The vast star-family to which our Sun
belongs—a family numbering anywhere from 30,000
millions to 300,000 millions—is gathered together
into a quite definite group, having the form of a
flattened ellipsoid—much the shape of a watch or
biscuit. Within this space the stars are scattered at
distances so great that the mind fails to form any

conception of them. A wireless signal from the Earth that would reach the Sun, 93 millions of miles away, in a few minutes, would take over four years to reach the very nearest star. And the dimensions of the whole group are such that a flash of light, or the same wireless signal, travelling 186,000 miles a second, would take 200,000 years to cross its longer diameter; in other words, if an observer were stationed on a star at the edge of the Galaxy, the twinkling at the opposite edge 500,000,000,000,000,000 miles away, which he might see, would be light which was emitted 200,000 years before.

And does this take us to the edge of the known Universe? Very far from it.   Our five-hundred-thousand-million-million-mile galaxy is but one of innumerable star-families scattered through space at distances compared to which the dimension just named sinks into insignificance. The Great Nebulae, which form so striking a feature of stellar photography, represent such star-families—ones which happen to be comparatively near to us.   Few of them appear to be so large or at so advanced a stage of evolution as our own Galaxy, and while they are estimated each to contain enough matter to form some two thousand million stars, much of this matter has not yet condensed, and still retains the form of glowing clouds of star-dust. In the great 100-inch telescope at Mount Wilson, some two millions of these two-thousand-million star-clusters can be counted, the furthest of them so far away that light takes about 140 millions of years to travel from them to us. In despair we ask, does this bring

us to the confines of the Universe? There is no
reason to think so. " The 200-inch telescope, which
it is hoped will shortly be built, having twice the
aperture of the present 100-inch, ought to probe
twice as far into space, and so may perhaps be
expected to show about eight times as many, or
16 million, nebulae." Is there then no limit whatever
to the Universe? According to Einstein's researches
there is, although we shall probably never have visible proof of it. Once the telescope is left behind, one
enters a region of mathematical and philosophical
speculation into which only few can pass.

Thus we range from the inconceivably minute to
the inconceivably great. The mind is staggered
equally by the vastness of the machine of which our
Earth, all-important to us, forms so insignificant a
fragment, and by the excessive minuteness of the
units—the atoms—of which the whole Universe is
built up. Whence did it arise? What does it mean?
" Sense knows not; Faith knows not; only that it is
through Mystery to Mystery, from God and to God."

DAY AND NIGHT IN EL VALLE.

As you stand at Güimar, on the southern coast of Tenerife, and look up the steep slope that ascends from the sea to some eight thousand feet, you see a gap in the sky-line sentinelled on either side by soaring pinnacles of jagged rock. This is the Garganta de Güimar (the Güimar Gate) or simply El Valle, one of the most impressive spots in the Canary Islands; a place almost terrifying in its savageness and the evidence it displays of having been till quite recently the scene of violent volcanic convulsions. It is a place not easy to explore, for the entrance lies five thousand feet above the Güimar hotels, and with even an early start the full heat of day is beating into this inferno of shadeless rocks before you reach it. We had had a few hours in El Valle on a former visit, following a long morning ride from Orotava across the backbone of Tenerife, and this brief glance at its tremendous precipices and peculiar flora made us resolved to find our way there again, with more time at our disposal, and better preparation against heat and cold. At Arafo, lying on the slope high above Güimar, we found a good jumping-off place—a tiny fonda (inn), its patio shaded by a dense roof of passion-flower and vine, its windowless bedrooms (the open door serves for window here) commanding wide views of mountain and ocean, and of the high serrated outline of Gran Canaria fifty miles away. In the evening we watched Venus in a sky of black velvet blazing as she never blazes with us, swinging lower and lower over the giant gateposts of El Valle and seemingly getting larger and larger as she sank, till suddenly, snap! and she was gone, in that clear air with never a moment of dimming.

Before dawn the voice of our hostess and the stamping of a mule tell us it is time to be stirring. The morning air stings like frost, and a candle in the patio burns without a quiver, lighting up the vine leaves. A cup of scalding coffee and we grope our way into the village street, which runs straight up the hill, nearly as steep as a ladder. The east is faintly yellow now, with a pale whitish gleam on the peaks far above us, and there is just light enough to see the rough paved road and to avoid the innumerable pitfalls. Sleeping-bags, food and water (the last most indispensable of all), are on the sturdy mule, whose driver, muffled to the eyes, stands like a grey shadow against a white house-wall. A handshake and a hearty " Hasta la vista " from our hostess, and we are off. Up through terraced irrigated fields of rye and potatoes into the higher zone of vines, where the sun springs up and floods the land with brightness. Two hours, and we are into the pine-woods, already glad of the cool shade which they afford. Groups of villagers pass us, coming down from their early forage-raid. They have started at two in the morning—men, women, and children—up the rough mountain tracks, have cut fresh herbs and bushes at dawn high above the forest zone, and are now returning for the day's work with huge bundles borne on their heads, or on the backs of mules; the woods re-echo with song and laughter and the tinkling of mule-bells. Another thousand feet and we emerge from the forest on to wide slopes of black ashes, bare save for sweet chestnuts, gnarled and dwarfed, scattered thinly over the hill-side. They too give out, and before us rises a cinder mountain—a thousand-foot cone of black velvet, with not even a leaf or blade to relieve its utter sterility. We plod through hot heavy cinders between the cinder hill and a deep ravine, cross a wide gravel fan with green bushes, and halt in a dry torrent-bed between low cliffs. A glance at watch and barometer—four thousand feet climbed in four hours; eight o'clock and time for breakfast, for here we will camp, in the middle of El Valle. Now we can look about us. A steeply-sloping oasis, a mile long and half a mile wide, seamed with ravines, covered with rocks, stones, and white and yellow kinds of broom. In front, the slope runs up to a steep barren hill of hardened mud, red, orange, and yellow, glowing in the sunlight. On the left a vertical cliff, two thousand feet high, with a saw-like edge against the blue sky, forms a straight and continuous wall. The right side of the valley is enclosed by a great rugged mountain nearly as steep; and behind us, down the slope, the view of the lower grounds and of the ocean is cut off by the black mountain of cinders past which we have climbed. Not a sign of man or of any living creature anywhere: only the miles of many-coloured rock shimmering in the sun, with the thin green of the valley-bottom to relieve the feeling that this is indeed Inferno, consecrate to plutonic forces, and banned to every form of life. The sun is beginning to burn, but in the ravine it is still cool. Fuel is plentiful and as dry as tinder. Coffee is soon ready. We watch our mulateer vanish on his homeward way, his beast laden with fresh branches of Retama (broom), and we are alone. I hurry off to explore before the heat of the day. Up a wild gorge, often turned back by vertical walls of rock. Over rough lava blocks and scattered volcanic bombs. Up smooth slopes of gravelly volcanic mud, so hard and steep that progress is almost impossible on account of slipping; one feels like a beetle trying to climb a bank of dry running sand. Finally into the main gorge at the head of the valley. Desperate ground this. Its floor is so steep that one climbs with hands as much as feet over a wilderness of fallen blocks of every colour, treading cautiously for fear of a miniature avalanche which might easily half bury one. The gaunt sides of the ravine, rent and riven, streaked yellow and red with sulphur and iron, rise on either side high into the sky. Here, often inaccessible, grow the plants we have come to seek—strange hybrid Sempervivums, seen on our previous visit, hitherto unknown and needing further study. One is dripping wet with the exertion and heat when, high up, one drops suddenly into a deep snow-drift, of all things, filling a sunless corner, a reminder of how cold the air is here a mile and a half above the sea, despite the burning sun.

Back at camp, my wife reports one living thing—
a small rat, rooting among the stones; how does
it maintain life in this dreadful place? Siesta follows
lunch, for the sun is flaming now, and the very
insects have crawled to shelter. When we rouse up
we spread our sleeping-bags and blankets on the
pocket of sand where we will sleep—the sand is
so hot that it burns one's fingers and makes it
painful to stand in one place. We botanize along
a shady cliff, and return at sunset, for supper by
moonlight. Then to bed, for the chill of night is
here already. The rocks and sand are now icy cold,
save where our blankets have been spread, where
a deliciously warm couch awaits us ... I awake in
the small hours. The moon has set; the stars blaze
and scintillate in a sky of blue-black velvet, the
jagged peaks above us ghostly and pale against it.
The silence is almost frightening. Suddenly a green
meteor dashes down the sky. Does one really hear
the swish of it; or is that fancy? It bursts and
vanishes, leaving a fading path behind; one is again
alone with the cliffs and the innumerable pin-point
suns. A long silence. Then a startling wild cry,
which re-echoes from the rocks, like no cry one
has ever heard before. What is it? Bird? Beast?
Or some elemental being in this dead home of
terrestrial convulsions? It comes not again. Only
once or twice the crash of a falling rock. . . . When
we wake the east is paling, down behind the black
cinder-cone. It is bitterly cold. We stumble up the
rough hill-side and crouch in blankets to watch the
sun rise. The light grows rapidly. Below us,

spreading to an infinitely far horizon, is a smooth ocean of cloud, dove-grey, delicately corrugated. At its distant edge, straight as if drawn with a ruler, is the dawn. First a yellow flush, soon a vivid rainbow of colour in horizontal bands—red lowest, then orange, yellow, green, blue, broadening and brightening. Suddenly all the cliffs and peaks around flush vivid rose-pink, and then with a blinding flash the sun is up, quivering, pouring lambent waves of gold across the valley. The effect on the cloud-ocean is almost immediate. Great billows arise, water-spouts of vapour writhe high into the air. Floods of glowing white mist advance and flow round the edges of the black cone; they submerge our valley, rise higher, break, wreathe round the dark crags far above, catch the light again and ascend as snowy clouds into the blue. The sun breaks through again, white now, not gold. Day is here, and with it we remember our chilled bodies, and that it is not yet five o'clock. Hot coffee is clearly indicated. Then off for a long morning's climbing among gigantic cliffs, returning with floral spoils, when once more the heat and glare become unbearable. But this time I have ascended to the cumbre (crowning ridge), and have seen the strange land that stretches thence for miles to where the great cone of The Peak rises to over 12,000 feet—miles of bare rock and cinders, red and yellow and purple, a rolling many-coloured desert, dotted with sprawling bushes of one plant only—the famous Retama of the high grounds, a broom-like shrub with thick rush-like twigs and myriads of white or pink flowers of overpowering fragrance. They say that in still weather the scent of the Retama sometimes fills the air at Puerto Orotava, by the sea seven thousand feet below.

The descent to our ravine camp is made in blinding heat, and once more we are glad to creep into rock-chinks and drowse away the afternoon, watching the shimmering cliffs, and the little dancing dust columns, and two great black and white vultures silently quartering the valley in wide circles. Then at last a faint song, very far away, and two moving specks down by the black volcano—it is Alexandro with his mule, come to break our solitude and end our vigil.

POPPIES AND PRASHACH.

Just as on our hillsides and mountains Heather and Gorse make a display of colour unequalled among our native plants, so in the farmland there is nothing to surpass a field scarlet with Poppies or yellow with the Prashach or Charlock. All of these four plants are so familiar to us that we accept without question the point that the second pair is as characteristic of the tilled ground as the first pair is of the untilled; but this point is an important one. Looking a little further into the matter, a number of facts emerge. The Heather and Gorse, and the plants of many kinds with which they are associated, are mostly of perennial duration; the Poppies and Charlock, and most of their companions, are annuals. Again, if a hillside is left to itself for a few years, little change occurs, save that the Heather and Gorse and their followers flourish and spread; the annual plants of the tillage make no attempt at invasion. But quite a different effect follows the abandonment by the farmer of the home of the Poppy and Charlock. If a piece of tillage be allowed to lie fallow, these plants and their annual companions may be still abundant in the following year, but mixed with them will be a number of young perennial plants from outside; next season the perennials will have increased largely, and in a few years more they will have ousted the annual plants entirely. It is clear from this that our Poppies and Charlock maintain themselves only with the aid of tillage operations; and an interesting problem arises. Tillage is, even in its most primitive form, of recent origin, dating back only to the Neolithic Period. But the plants are far older than this. What, then, did these plants do when there was no tillage, when the whole country was in a " state of nature "? It is, after all, only a few thousand years since Neolithic man first began to scratch the ground and sow seeds in the scratches: Poppies have been in existence ten or fifty or a hundred times longer than that.

What do we mean when we speak of a " state of nature " in our country? As a matter of fact, we mean a state of forest. Ireland lies within a broad zone extending across central and northern Europe whose weather is characterised by a succession of westerly or south-westerly cyclones, which sweep in from the Atlantic, both in summer and in winter, bearing much rain. Where there is a sufficient rainfall tree-growth is the prevailing type of vegetation from the Arctic Circle to the Equator; and trees formerly covered the greater part of our country, as they did, and in many places still do, the surface of Europe down to about the Alps. Forest country could never have been a home for the sun-loving annual plants which we are discussing. With a less abundant rainfall, grassland of one kind or another is widely spread over the world. But this is a close crowded type of vegetation, composed almost entirely of perennial plants, one in which our vagrant annuals would have an equally poor chance of obtaining a footing. If we pass on to regions of still lower rainfall—say the basin of the Mediterranean and southward towards the Sahara, or eastward to the deserts of Persia and Arabia—we find ourselves in a different climate and a different vegetation. While the winters may be cool, the summers are very hot and dry. Under these conditions a continuous carpet of vegetation no longer covers the ground. Plants tend to grow singly or in clumps, with an increasing space between as dryness increases. And we find the flora tending to break up into two groups which adopt quite different ways of preserving their existence. The perennials save themselves from drought by developing very long roots, and often by shortening their aerial parts. Frequently they store up water in very fleshy roots or stems or leaves, or protect their leaves and stems by coverings of hair or wax. Thus equipped, they can endure the fierce heat of summer. The other group, considering prevention better than cure, adopts a different manœuvre, and dodges the dry season altogether. They arise from seed as soon as the first autumn rain falls, grow during the cool winter, flower in the early spring, and ere the scorching summer supervenes they have ripened and scattered their seed. Then they die, and the drought-resisting seed remains to give rise to a new generation in the autumn. This life-history is as common in the plants of semi-desert places as it is uncommon in the woodlands and grasslands of wetter areas.

Again, when tillage was first practised, in Mesopotamia or Egypt, and spread along the Mediterranean under the Greeks and Romans, the new conditions which it introduced proved as suitable to the habits of the annual plants as they were unsuitable to the perennials. Periodical digging or ploughing of the land was fatal to the latter, but the annuals with their rapid and abundant seeding seized upon the open ground and were able to run through their complete life-cycle ere the next turning-over of the surface. Babylon and Carthage had the same weed problem that we have. Theophrastus and Pliny write as learnedly of Dodder and Broomrape, hoeing and stubbing (according to their lights), as the pundits of the present day.

The great forest-barrier of central and northern Europe, which held up Cæsar's legions, delayed also the spread of agriculture and of its camp-followers the weeds. But as the forests vanished before the attacks of the husbandman, and were succeeded by tillage, the weeds advanced concurrently, for the conditions which meant death to the native perennial flora meant life to them. So now we have quite an extensive special vegetation, derived, to a large degree, from the Mediterranean region, the home of the older civilisations, and dependent on the continuance of husbandry for its continued existence. Poppies and Prashach, Fumitories, Valerianellas, Catchflies, Melilots, Corn Bluebottle, Chamomiles, Toad-flaxes, Veronicas, Goosefoots of many kinds, are our welcome or unwelcome guests, according as we are flower-lovers or farmers. And with increased inter-communication, immigrants still come to us, often from lands undreamed of by

Theophrastus. The most successful of all the recent colonists, the Rayless Feverfew, has crossed the Atlantic from the United States; and even distant New Zealand is contributing her quota to our alien population.

IN PRAISE OF FLYING.

COLONEL RUSSELL'S experimental flight from Galway to London last year,* with American mails, excited in this country a passing ripple of interest in the question of aviation. "Ireland stirred in its Celtic dream," as Arnold Bennett would put it; but by now most of us have comfortably returned to sleep, despite the efforts of an active young Aero Club. Buzzing aeroplanes are very rare in our skies, and we accept with unconcerned complacency the announcements about aviation being the mode of travel of the future, and so on, much as we accept warnings as to the imminence of the Day of Judgment. Few of us realise that we are witnesses of a revolution compared to which Stephenson's "Rocket" and the arrival of railways, which so excited our grandparents, was a commonplace. We do not see enough of flying here to accept it as a practical proposition, as a matter of direct concern to each of us. The personal view is generally that flying is still an enthusiast's fad and a dangerous adventure, suitable only for daredevils who try to cross the Atlantic in open boats or to swim the Niagara rapids. We do not realise the extent of the regular commercial air-service which has been developed on the Continent. Yet the 1930 flying programme issued by the Deutsche Luft-Hansa Company, the largest of the Continental concerns,

* August, 1929.

shows more than six hundred daily passenger flights between European cities, over a network of routes and junctions almost comparable with that of the railways. In addition, there are tri-weekly or bi-weekly or weekly services running out over eastern Europe, and extending away to Baku, Samarkand, Irkutsk, Kabul, and distant India. The aerodrome at most of the larger Continental cities becomes nowadays more and more like a great railway station, as yet not nearly so populous, but infinitely more stimulating and picturesque, with planes constantly arriving from and departing for every part of Europe.

Here in Ireland these things are far-off, and we are content to allow them to develop, and to let others risk their necks in what we still regard at best as pioneer work. Yet, this is the time to fly, while there still remains something of novelty and excitement about it, just as there was about railways and steamers in the eighteen-forties, and while the air companies have still to make good with the public, and consequently use every effort to have things convenient and pleasant for their customers. As compared with railway and steamboat travel, especially during the busy season, the difference in comfort is vast if you travel by air. At the office, always situated in some central place in the city, you are received with courtesy. No waiting in a queue before a ticket office, no scrambling at a baggage room; tickets and a receipt for luggage are given; usually you are solemnly weighed for some occult reason; then a comfortable motor 'bus whisks you out to the aerodrome, somewhere on the city outskirts. There you sit in a pleasant restaurant, mostly in the open air, under a big umbrella with gay flower-beds—dahlias and petunias and sweet-pea—to right and left, and watch the planes arriving and departing until your plane is announced. There the monster stands, glistening in its aluminium armour, mechanics swarming over it, using an oil-can here and a spanner there. You are shown into the cabin with its double row of light arm-chairs, with a narrow corridor between, and on the outer side a window to each seat. Word is given, the plane taxies off to the down-wind end of the ground. Then a flag waves, the engine roars out, the machine rushes across the grass, and in a few moments bumping stops, and you see the ground falling away beneath; the plane swings round into its course, and you settle down for your journey. No dark and noisy railway station, no scramble for seats, no stuffy and crowded compartments, no dust, no heat, no changing (if your journey includes a sea-passage) from train to boat, and from boat to train. You rise at Croydon, for instance, and in three and a half hours you drop into Amsterdam; you rise at Amsterdam, and within six hours you are in Sweden. And on arrival, no bother about customs or passports; all is done in two or three minutes, and you are again in a motor, which drops you at some central point, or as often as not, at any place you may desire; and all included in the price of the ticket. I have ascended or descended at Amsterdam, Basle, Belgrad, Brussels, Buda-Pesth, Cologne, Croydon, Dortmund, Essen, Erfurt, Frankfort, Geneva, Hanover, Innsbruck, Leipzig, Lyons,

Magdeburg, Munich, Nuremberg, Paris, Rotterdam, Vienna, Zurich; always the same courtesy, promptness, absence of crowds and of hurry, pleasant open-air waiting-rooms and green expanses, instead of the noisy, crowded, smoky railway stations that to so many of us are inseparable from holidays.

As to the air journeys themselves. There is among people who have never flown much talk of air-sickness. In all the thirty or so planes in which I have travelled, I have only once seen anyone air-sick, and that was an anæmic young girl, on the most bumpy journey I have ever had. There are people who can be sea-sick in a ship in dry dock; no doubt they would be air-sick in a plane on the ground. Such folk should avoid not only aeroplanes but ships, and in many cases railway trains as well, if they desire comfort. Air travel is very like being in a fast motor-launch in water that is calm, save for an occasional slight disturbance; now and then there is a curious little downward jerk, now and then a slight swaying motion—that is the usual experience, so far as some thousands of miles of travel in planes large and small, British, Dutch, French, Austrian and German, can show. There is, of course, the noise; formerly this was so bad—such an overpowering roar—that one could not even shout to one's neighbour; but now with improved construction it is little worse than a *noisy* train, and conversation is usually possible, though it is a vigorous exercise for the lungs.

As one drones along thousands of feet above the earth, one gets new impressions of sky architecture;

clouds and haze take on fresh forms as one views
them from an equal altitude, or from above. Accustomed as we are to see only the underside of cloud-
masses, there is a never-failing fascination in view-
ing them from new standpoints. The study of the
land from the air is wholly interesting as one drifts
across the Continent high over hills and valleys. I
never appreciated the extraordinary industry and
skill that have reclaimed Holland from the sea until
I flew over some of the half-land-half-water areas of
that remarkable country. The topography of the
Danube between Vienna and Buda-Pesth, with all
the age-long windings of the great river, now
deserted and silted up, still clearly showing, was a
fascinating study. Best of all a flight from Munich
to Innsbruck across the Bavarian Alps, when we
crossed the snow-streaked peaks at 10,000 feet, and
finally circled down and down into the great gorge
of the Inn. Then there was a wild journey over the
Thüringer Wald in very bad weather, when we crept
along under, and then soared above, the hurrying
masses of rain-cloud; and an idyllic evening crossing of the Harz Mountains to Cologne, when after
passing the hills we soared higher and higher, a
speck against a cloudless golden sunset, until the
petrol ran out, impelling our eagle to a hurried and
ignominious swoop on Dortmund, eight thousand
feet below. When one is off the main routes there
may be little amenities that add greatly to the
interest of the journey. Flying across South Germany one of our pilots kept handing in to us from
the cockpit notes of interesting places and things

which we passed. Thus we identified and viewed as on a map the lovely little old town of Nördlingen, still almost wholly enclosed within its intact medieval walls, with their gateways and flanking towers. Again, some years earlier, passing over Zeebrugge, we saw as in a diagram the historic mole and docks, and the sunken British ships still lying on the sandy bottom under the clear water. Many of the larger cities, Vienna, Munich, Buda-Pesth, look magnificent from the air, and one gets new impressions of their lay-out and situation, and of the noble proportions of the great medieval cathedrals—the Stephanskirche, the Marienkirche—and the way in which these dominate the crowded mass of petty houses around them.

In the open country, the variation in the lay-out of the fields and buildings is a source of continual interest. In some areas the farmhouses are scattered about, each set on its own land as in our own country. In other districts, the houses are collected entirely into villages, and the eye ranges over miles of waving crops with never a building or fence to break the kaleidoscopic carpet of oats and beet and potatoes and what-not; and the distribution of the crops themselves and its meaning alone gives much food for thought.

Lastly, a word as to cost. On paper, air travel appears as somewhat above first-class rail, but if your time is worth anything, it works out a good deal cheaper than that. The pace averages about three times that of a fast train; more than three times, if Channel crossings are also concerned. By using the air you avoid night travelling or its alternative, a night in a hotel, frequently also expensive meals in the train, and you arrive fresh and vigorous, not jaded, hot, and dusty. If you are in a hurry and have far to go, you can use the aeroplane by day and the train by night. That is how you get from New York to San Francisco nowadays in forty-eight hours; but one of the greatest advantages of the air services is that on long journeys it allows a good night's rest, and yet brings you there as quickly as the old day-and-night through journey.

I remember when I thought the jog across France or Germany towards the Alps, in the holiday season, a penance; now it is a delight. Danger? If you scent danger, you need not sniff at aeroplanes; the streets of Dublin or Paris will provide as much of that as you have any use for. Nowadays we are all dwellers on the slopes of Etna, and our little life is bounded by a 'bus.

CANARIAN VIGNETTES.

FOR the final five hundred feet of the ascent the path is very steep, and the mules clamber and stumble up the roughly paved zigzag track which climbs to the Degollada, or pass, on the knife-edge ridge above. The precipitous slopes to right and left face full south, and even now, in May, all the pretty annual plants which decorated the rocks are brown and dried. The autumn rains will wake their seeds to activity; through the winter months they will grow vigorously; February and March will see them in bloom, and before our home annuals are thinking of pushing up a tentative blossom their life-cycle will have run its course. But the hot rocks are still covered with plants of many sorts which rejoice in the dry sub-tropical conditions which prevail here. Notable among these are members of the Sempervivum group. The cliffs are dotted with thousands of Greenovias, with their rosettes of blue-grey leaves and fountains of golden flowers. Even more abundant is *Sempervivum subplanum,* with large downy rosettes and spires of soft yellow blossoms. The glaucous *S. Castello-Paivae* is here also, forming little round grey bushes with pinkish-white blooms; the dark green sticky *S. viscatum,* its golden flowers not yet showing; and still another white-flowered species as yet undescribed.[1]   Numerous

1. *S. gomerense* Praeger.

other fleshy plants are here too, and the vegetation resembles the Succulent House at Kew, glorified by glowing sunlight and magnificent mountain scenery.

We cross the pass to the northern slope—only a dozen paces—and what a contrast! One plunges at once into deep dark woods, through which the wind blows cool and damp. The trees, mainly Heath (*Erica arborea*) and Laurel (*Laurus canariensis*), are hung with dripping moss, among which many plants cling as epiphytes. The ground is one great fernery, with grand arching fronds 4 or 5 feet long. A dozen species are here, from the massive *Woodwardia radicans* to the tiny annual *Gymnogramma leptophylla*; while the crevices of the rocks are lined with the Maidenhair and the curious undivided fronds of its cousin, *Adiantum reniforme*. Down the steep slopes *Ranunculus cortusæfolius,* with sprays of large golden blossom on 3-ft. stems, runs riot. After the glare of the southern slope our eyes require a minute or two to become accustomed to the dim green light, and then we discover innumerable smaller treasures—mosses and hepatics and delicate tiny herbs, all sparkling with dew, and green as emerald, while the wet wind that feeds them moans through the branches overhead.

We step once more across the pass, and we are back in the burning glare, windless and quivering, among the grey desert plants and the hot rocks. A black and white vulture soars, a thin wisp of smoke rises from the blue valley-bottom two thousand feet below, and far beyond, like a red blot, are the roofs of San Sebastian, with the dim line of the Atlantic behind them.

A tall young peasant has joined my companions at the summit, his long *lanca,* an 8-ft. jumping-pole with an iron point, in his hand, his heavy double-pocketed embroidered saddlebag at his feet. " Take care," he calls to me as I climb towards them, " that ground is dangerous "—as indeed it is. We chat a little, and then he swings his bag across his shoulders, waves a friendly farewell and, scorning the path, is off down the slope like a chamois.

LAVA AND CINDERS.

Our camel grunts disgustedly at having three people imposed on him, but we pack on—one slung on either side, and one perched giddily between— and jolt, jolt! he is on his feet. The worst of a camel is that he gets up in jerks, first one end and then the other, and without practice one forgets which end goes up first. Consequently if one is absent-minded one may find oneself in the dust with disconcerting suddenness. We turn our backs on the houses and palm trees of Yaiza, and the lava confronts us instantly. This is only an arm of the great flows which fill all the valleys to the northward. It is barely a mile wide, but without the rough path that we are about to travel, that mile would be utterly impassable. The lava is like an ice-jam turned into black stone, a confused jumble of crests and troughs and great slabs up-ended or capsized, and so hard and glassy that one cannot so much as touch it without torn clothes and cut fingers. Our camel swings slowly and unconcernedly along the rough track, over mounds and into hollows, while our eyes seek in vain for any trace of life, animal or vegetable. We see, at last, a tiny fringe of green along a crack on a horizontal slab. It is a fern, of all things—an Adder's-tongue (*Ophioglossum polyphyllum*). How does it survive in this blasted place, where in summer the heat radiated from the black rock is mere torture?

We near the opposite shore of our lava ocean. Gaunt bare hills face us, red and yellow and black, with a curiously smooth, velvety surface, on which these tints pass imperceptibly from one to another. We are soon on the slopes, to find that the mountains are composed of (or at least thickly covered with) cinders, of a uniform fineness, and packed so firmly that our footsteps hardly leave an impression. Again the eye ranges in search of life. Here is a solitary bush of the prickly *Zollikoferia spinosa,* all thorns, after the manner of *Alyssum spinosum* or *Vella spinosa*, dotted with tiny fragrant lettuce-like flowers, and few minute leaves. It is long before we see another plant, but here is a venturesome little colony of another desert thing, *Polycarpæa Teneriffæ*. We ascend steeply now (the camel being relieved of its encumbrances and turned loose to meditate on the strangeness of things). To the left rises a grove of slender, erect stems on a steep, hot cinder slope. To our great surprise this is a British plant, *Juncus acutus,* which we associate at home with damp hollows in seaside dunes. Now we skirt the rim of a great crater, treading on a yellow sulphurous crust. Our camel-driver feels with his hand, and says " This will do." He scratches a hole a foot deep, burning his fingers in the process, drops in some eggs to cook for lunch. Then, turning his back on the wonderful view, he sits down and lights a cigar.

Our eyes wander over miles of many-tinted mountains and deep craters and broad black plains devoid of tree or shrub or herb, for these are recent outpourings, some only two hundred years old, and the ground is still hot in places, as it is here. To the south the hills are different, for they are much older. The surface has weathered into a thin soil, and at least in winter it is green with crops on the lower part, with native herbs above. The fields and walls are grateful, for they remind us more of home and less of Dante's Inferno. " Los huevos son cocidos," says the guide, and we fall to.

MADRE DE LORO.

From the crest of the ridge we look back down the tortuous mountain valley up which we have toiled, with its great rock masses, its patches of trees and bushes, and little terraced fields poised here and there on the steep slopes. Turning again, a glorious view lies in front of us. The ridge on which we stand sweeps away to the left in a semi-circle, varying from 3,000 ft. to 4,000 ft. in height, and enclosing a broad basin some miles in diameter, filled with dense unbroken forest—a finer forest scene than can be found anywhere else on the Canary Islands, for Gomera surpasses the other islands in the extent and luxuriance of its woods. Under the guidance of our Canario friend, we plunge downward into the

cool shade. The composition of the forest is very
interesting, for all the species which grow here are
unfamiliar to us, at least as forest trees. Four members of the laurel family are conspicuous—Viñatico
(*Persea indica*), Loro (*Laurus canariensis*), Barbu-
sano (*Appolonias canariensis*) and Til (*Oreodaphne
fœtens*). The first two of these are particularly striking, forming glorious lofty columns. The beautiful
Davallia (*D. canariensis*) and the Common Polypody
of our English rocks (*P. vulgare*) cling to their
trunks, and a species of Sempervivum (*S. dichoto-
mum*) perches high up on the moss-grown boles and
makes yellow splashes of colour, outshone by the
scarlet fallen leaves of the Viñatico. Among the
other native trees we see the Mocan (*Visnea moca-
nera*), the Hija, which we call Portugal Laurel
(*Prunus lusitanicus*), a fine large-leaved holly,
Acebiño (*Ilex canariensis*), Palo Blanco (*Notelæa
excelsa*), Aderno (*Heberdenia excelsa*), Marmolan
(*Pleiomerus canariensis*) and several Ericaceæ—
Madroño (*Arbutus canariensis*), *Myrica Faya,* Brezo
(*Erica arborea*). The last named, the Tree Heather,
perhaps interests us most, for we are rather proud
of having at home a bush of it, ten feet high, which
covers itself in early spring with fragrant grey-white
blossom. But here it forms groves, fifty feet in
height. I try to get my arms round one of the
trunks, but my hands do not meet, for it is seven feet
in circumference.

A diversion occurs. Our guide steps out on a
projecting spur, surveys the valley below, puts his
fingers to his lips, and gives a long complicated

whistle. We listen with attention, for this is the famous whistling language of Gomera. The sound echoes from the woods opposite, is repeated by more distant hills, and dies away. The whistler listens, shakes his head, and calls again. Whee, whee, whee—whee, whee, whee, whee-e-e-e, floats out over the forest. No reply. We resume our march, and half a mile farther on the shrill call is given again. This time a faint clear answer comes up from far below. " Good," says our guide; " I was telling Juan to bring a cheese to the luncheon-place," he explains. Presently we debouch into an open glade, where a sight greets us most rare in the Canaries—a broad, cool, rippling stream. The hot sunlight dances on the shallows, and the sides are lined with ferns of many kinds. " Here we eat," says Don Pedro. Bread and wine, sardines and gofio, appear from mysterious saddle-bags. The gofio is kneaded with water from the stream, and lunch is ready. While we eat, a venerable man strides up, his long *lanca* in one hand, in the other a fresh cheese wrapped in a clean napkin. " Ah, Juan," says our guide, " you have come."

After lunch we are called aside to see one of the curiosities of the forest. A great Laurel (Bay, we would call it) rises solitary, and on its trunk, a few feet up, is a curious outgrowth forming a ring round the stem—a series of fleshy leafless forked growths, neither roots nor branches. They are soft and downy to the touch, and remind one of a deer's horns while still in the velvet. They come away easily from the trunk, and we break one across. The section shows a uniform green watery tissue, like the stem of a succulent plant. It has the fragrant scent of Bay, and is clearly portion of the tree, not a fungus parasite or anything of that sort. It is a puzzle, and we appeal to our guide for information. " Madre de Loro " (Mother of Laurel), says he. What is it? Frankly I do not know, nor have I discovered any reference to it in the books to which I have had access. No doubt the men of science have worked it all out—probably those industrious Germans to whom we owe much of our knowledge of the plants of the Canaries. But I am not sure that I do not prefer leaving it there, a mystery among those beautiful forests.

BEFORE BREAKFAST.

THE wallpaper is disturbing, and haunts me even when I close my eyes. It is not so much the huge purple roses on a dull olive-green background as the vista which appears between them—a colonnade with four Corinthian columns loaded with pink gloxinias as large as cabbages, and backed by a zig-zag trellis fence in outline strangely like a dachshund. The symmetry of the pattern, with recurring diagonal blotches from floor to ceiling, recalls a recent air photograph of American soldiers at physical drill, spread over a wide parade ground. I have a vision of innumerable dachshunds geometrically disposed, waving clubs rhythmically to the strains of the "Star-Spangled Banner," and at this I jerk wide awake. A warm orange gleam on the edge of the window-frame tells that the sun has risen, so I slip on clothes and boots and descend the crazy stairs with portentous creakings. There is an autumnal nip in the air, and a diaphanous mist. At the door of the inn Usnach, the young greyhound, is lying in wait. Usnach is a dear personal friend, but one could wish that her appetite were not so catholic. The loss of my sponge was easily explained. "Ah, sure, it'll be Usnach; she does take an odd thing." A cap was the next victim. "Well now, she's fond of a sponge, but she never took a cap before; are ye sure ye had a cap?" As it was the only covering that had screened my head from the fury of the elements for a week, I was quite sure. But when a woollen sweater disappeared there was trouble. All Usnach's favourite haunts were scoured in vain by solicitous hand-maidens. " Sure she couldn't have it et; ye must have left it somewhere." Certainly I had—on a chair in the bedroom. Usnach was absolved in the eyes of the family; but as she appeared rather abstracted and inactive during the day—like the Scotchman, A hae ma doots.

On the telegraph wires in front of the door the swallows are gathered as usual. A hundred of them sit there all facing the same way, stretching wings and preening feathers and twittering unceasingly. It is nearly time for them to be off, and they hold conferences every morning as to sea routes and weather reports and the vexed question of return tickets. A late comer alights with his head facing the wrong way, and horrified by this breach of decorum darts off and is seen no more. But why do a score or more pretend to be building nests against the whitewashed wall under the eave? They have actually outlined new foundations in mud, and they flutter incessantly about this unseasonable architecture, while others sit above on the slate roof and scoff ... Another week and they will all have vanished on their migration flight, that mystery of mysteries.

The only occupant of the village street is a white goat, surreptitiously nibbling somebody's Michaelmas daisies. Usnach prances off with backward glances—the invitation may not be refused. The thatched post office seems fast asleep, but as we pass, an early cyclist dismounts and taps at a window open at the bottom. A hand is protruded holding a bundle of letters, which are pocketed, and the cyclist vanishes as noiselessly as he came. Thus does the Business of the State go on unceasingly while citizens sleep. Beyond the last house, the great Norman moat rises close to the road, steep-sided, flat-topped, with an ample bailey of lesser height on its northern side. The grass is drenched with dew, which sparkles around one's lanky shadow, and forms a silver aura round one's elongated head. Many autumn flowers are here—Knapweed and Scabious, Cat's-ear and the dainty Felwort, making a brave show in early September. The sturdy Dandelions, too, have awakened from their summer drowsing, and entered upon their nine-months' season of bloom, to cheer alike the dull days of winter and the joyousness of spring. Usnach successfully chases a leisurely cat—evidently an old friend—into an apple-tree, and we proceed. Beyond a little planting of pines, dark with shadow, is a shallow valley filled with hazy sunlight. The more distant fields are lost in silver mist, but in the foreground the haycocks and corn-stooks stand out in brightest gold; they glitter in the golden sunlight. And from each haycock a plume of tenuous white vapour rises straight up in the still air, wavering at the top and slowly dissolving. It is as if the wraiths of the dead flowers were ascending to some aerial Nirvana, there to await re-incarnation in the succeeding spring...Usnach spies a friend in a field on the right. It is a stunted brown animal like a Noah's Ark dog. It stands rigid on four stiff stumpy legs, a rapid quivering of its rod-like tail alone betraying the intensity of its emotions, while the greyhound with eel-like contortions of her body weaves a circle round it three times thrice, barking herself all out of shape the while. A water-hen, scandalised by so rude an irruption on the morning peace, crosses the road hurriedly with an air of offended dignity, and the white patch on her tail vanishes among the sedges.

Near the village, derelict on the grassy margin of the road, is a green waggon enclosing the rusty machinery of a merry-go-round, a wagtail perched perkily on the top of its broken and despondent funnel. On the sides of the cart one can still trace daring and complicated designs which might have made the scribes of the Book of Kells green with envy; but much of their zoomorphic exuberance is now concealed behind fascinating promises on tattered squares of green or pink paper of the millennium which will immediately ensue if only you will give your vote to Fianna Fáil or to Clann Eireann. Down an adjoining lane stands the counterpart of the first waggon, packed with flattened dappled steeds with prancing hoofs and flashing eyes. Their days of prancing are over; no more will that steam-driven blare of discordant sound spur them to fresh exertions; never again will the clamour of delighted children speed their fiery onrush. One could scarce believe that a deserted merry-go-round could look so woe-begone. Perhaps I am getting hungry.

As we re-pass the great moat a little figure appears on the summit, silhouetted against the sky—a tiny barefoot girl, lightly clad, her gauzy dress and yellow hair blowing in the wind. She calls "Usnach, Usnach," and the dog darts to her; together they dance recklessly down the steep flower-strewn slope, and vanish behind an old thorn tree in a sudden silence. Was it really a child I saw, or a fairy? "Ye'd need to be half a goat to be ayqual to that one," says a voice at my elbow. An old man is sitting blinking on a stool at his house door. I get a momentary glimpse of orange nasturtiums, new whitewash, bright yellow thatch, of a young girl in a blue cotton frock with a wonderful mop of red-gold hair, a cup of milk in her hand. Then something cannons violently into me, and a wet paw on the back of my neck tells that Usnach has returned.

In the berried yew beside the church the missel-thrushes are very busy, flapping and clutching at the red fruit—am I the only creature in all West-meath to whom breakfast comes not?

An upper window creaks, and the sergeant of the Gárda protrudes a shining morning face and sur-veys benignly the winding village street. "Morning, Jack; how's the family this morning?" The man addressed has a moustache like an old Viking, and a stiff leg; in one hand is a pail full of some foodstuff; in the other he grasps a mighty staff. He turns to me. "Did ever ye see a litter of pigs one day old?" No, that is outside the range of my limited experi-ence. So he leads the way down a few steps to

where two half-doors in a shed subtend each a
square black space. There is a scuffle inside, and one
of the spaces is suddenly filled by the head and
shoulders of a huge boar, its feet on the door ledge,
its small eyes fixed on us malevolently. " Not that
one," says the man. I peer into the other chamber,
where fourteen tiny piglets disport themselves about
an unwieldly grovelling mass of pink flesh. A yellow kitten has joined their gambols, and they are
having an uproarious time. Delightful little creatures, to be the offspring of so hideous a mother!
" They're all right yet," says the man, " so long as
she doesn't sthep on one of them . . . Do ye know
anything, sir, about white-faced bullocks?"

But now a silvery tinkle makes itself audible above
the slumberous rumblings of the mother pig, and
suddenly the world seems brighter. " That'll be yer
breakfast," says my companion; " an' yer lavin'
to-morra? To-morra ye'll be back in the big
shmoke. Well, A wouldn't care to live in a big town
meself. But if ye have to, perhaps Dublin's the least
worst." A waft of frying bacon comes across the
road. It makes me feel like a murderer, in the
presence of those fourteen innocents; but, like Mac-
beth, I go; the bell invites me.

KARLAK.

As you sail over the Aegean Sea, between the tall islands of Thasos and Samothrace, you may see the dark ridge of Karlak far to the northward, beyond the low shores of the Greek mainland. Or if you stand by the ruined block-houses on the old Turkish frontier near Philippopolis and look southward, you see it from the other side, rising boldly beyond the sea of mountains which form the southern part of the Rhodope region. With a good glass on a clear morning you may observe that it is clothed with forest in the lower parts, with tall crags of grey rock rising boldly above. In days not yet distant this dominating ridge lay well within Turkish territory, which may account for the absence of scientific information concerning it; but during the last five-and-twenty years frontiers in the Balkans have melted and re-crystallized more than once, and Karlak (or Gümürdzinski Karlak, to give it its full title) is at present half Greek, half Bulgarian. Bulgaria possesses some able and energetic botanists, who had long cast curious eyes at this distant and unexplored hill, but the absence of railways, roads, and inns over a wide area surrounding the mountain interposed a barrier not readily surmounted. When the writer and a friend from Kew Gardens reached Sofia early in a recent August, an opportunity occurred, for a Bulgarian engineer had re-opened an old Roman lead and zinc mine well down

in the region of the mountain, and offered to the
Sofia botanists and ourselves the hospitality of his
half-finished camp.   Arrangements were speedily
made, and our little party of six—the two authors of
the recently published *Flore de la Bulgarie,* with Mr.
Turrill and myself and our wives—took the night
train southward.   The third class carriages on the
Simplon-Orient express are fumigated daily ever
since a clear connection has been established
between certain minute creatures and the spread of
typhus, but the first and second class are exempt
from this degrading treatment and in consequence
the train brings back from Constantinople passengers
other than men. The corridor, though full of mos-
quitoes, was found preferable to the coupé; and we
were glad when the morning sunlight revealed to
our sleepless eyes the rocky bluffs that rise out of
the plain over Philippopolis. We did not tarry in
this busy town, with its tall modern buildings, Turkish hovels, and people of a dozen nationalities. A
cup of coffee and we were off in an elderly motor
post-waggon; across fifteen miles of mountain-
rimmed plain, through fields of rice, maize, sun-
flowers, vines, tobacco, hemp, with parties of gypsies
encamped along the road.   Then a picturesque
village and a rushing river, and we enter a great
mountain defile.   The road, dusty and bumpy
beyond description, twists and turns under limestone cliffs; it is crowded with traffic, and so narrow that when vehicles meet it is a choice of being
squeezed against the rock or hanging perilously
above the roaring stream; and over all the white

dust hangs thick like a fog. The midday meal—dried fish, bread, and wine—is taken at a roadside hostelry, crowded with teamsters and travellers, and we are off again, climbing up the widening valley in a clearer atmosphere. At length pines appear, and we crawl through dark woods and emerge into lovely park-like country, with undulating flower-filled meadows and groves of pine and beach. We cross a col and suddenly below us is a forest-filled valley a thousand feet deep; beyond it range upon range of hills, and on the horizon for the first time our destination, Karlak, a serrated ridge dominating the southern view. The road, built by the Germans during the war, works its way down the precipitous slopes by wide detours, and a long steep descent down a narrow valley brings us to Ustovo, where we alight and stretch ourselves after seventy miles of rough mountain roads. A picturesque and primitive place this, its narrow street edged with cramped little shops open in front. In one we see the baker pushing loaves into his oven; in the next an old Turk sits cross-legged among his stock of rugs, silks, and what not; everywhere is the din of hammers where metal-workers are beating out copper into graceful jars and bowls and coffee-pots. Heavy-laden waggons creak past, the horses gay with blue leather trappings and hung with bells, not for ornament, but to scare away the wolves in winter. The village street is full of passengers on horseback or on foot, swaggering Turks, burly Bulgars, Greeks, Pomaks. Before the sun sinks we contrive an hour's botanizing on hills almost too steep to climb, and

then are led to a pleasant house among apple-trees
where we are to lodge for the night. It *looks* as
clean as a new pin, but alas! ... It is a sleepless
party which assembles at six next morning for
breakfast of dry bread, sheep's milk, and sheep's
milk cheese. Mules are ready, with a waggon for
the ladies, and we are off away down the valley, up,
across and down another, and up a third, till we
cross a stream on a high single-arch bridge just wide
enough for a horseman, and rounding an old building, find ourselves among a multitude of people. The
village consists of one small square full of trees. It
is market-day, and the place is crammed with men
and horses, and goods of all sorts spread on the
ground—no women, for this is a Pomak settlement.
The Pomaks are Bulgarian in race and speech, but
Turkish in everything else—religion, dress, customs.
The headman receives us with grave courtesy,
Turkish coffee is provided, and we sit in the shade
and watch the busy scene, which as regards both
dramatis personæ and setting is picturesque in the
extreme. Beyond this village there is merely a riding track, so our ladies join us on mule-back. On for
miles up the narrowing valley, then a long tortuous
climb through beech forest and suddenly we are at
the pass. Behind us stretches half Bulgaria, ridge
behind ridge; in front, beyond a Bulgarian foreground, rises Karlak, nearer now, so that we can see
the grey crowning crags; and dim behind it shim-
mers the Aegean Sea. Here we are greeted by our
genial engineer host, M. Savoff, who leads the way
along a mountain spur to where the skeletons of

wooden huts indicate the site of his mine. " Hier
keine Wanzen, nur Flöhe," he assures us (he has
heard of our fierce fighting of the two preceding
nights), and hurries off to speed supper. The blazing sunset fades, and the dining-room—a roof without walls—is lighted by a petroleum flare. Then by
starlight we cut bracken for beds on the floor and
sleep as one does after three days and two nights
without it. Next day we explore the Roman work-
ings, which are extensive. Coins of 200 B.C. have
been found here, and fragments of pottery of the
same date are lying about. The Romans knew good
ore when they saw it—here is plenty of stuff with
50 per cent. of lead and zinc, and some silver also.
But how did they transport it across the sea of
mountains which stretches in every direction? In
the afternoon we botanize, and our ladies pay visits
of state to some of the Turkish women in their
close seclusion. But Karlak beckons us, and on the
following day we leave our womenkind at the mine
and on foot make our way down the wooded valleys
to the large village of Daridere, where we are hospi-
tably entertained by the excise officer. In the evening we dine with the aristocrats at the local club
(which consists, in summer at least, of a few tables
in an orchard beside the stream)—the military com-
mandant, the mayor (a Bulgar), the deputy mayor (a
Turk), the excise officer, the forestry inspector, etc.
In honour of the occasion, the deputy mayor offi-
ciates as waiter. The forestry inspector volunteers
to guide us across the roadless country to our goal;
the army offers us horses. Later we repair to the

ball-room (a smooth field) where dancing is in progress. A great circle of dancers, hands joined—
young men and girls, some clad in western fashions,
some in local costume, soldiers, children, policemen,
students; back and forwards they go, in and out, to
the music of the bagpipes played Irish-ways, by
bellows under the arm.

Early next morning we are off on horses and
mules, and strike southward by rough tracks across
hilly country. Our plan is to hit the Græco-Bulgarian
frontier, and then work eastward along the frontier
path. Till the afternoon we jog up hill and down
dale, through beech forests, over rocky scarps, along
dry river-beds. Finally to a hill-top and a military
post, with rusty wire entanglements and dilapidated
trenches, but alert sentries, for it is only a year since
there was a row followed by an incursion of Greek
troops and a considerable loss of life and property.
The soldiers prepare a meal for us, a thick soup of
beans and paprika—one big bowl, many spoons—followed by scrambled eggs. Then we face eastward,
and start along the ridge, a frontier guard leading the
way. A few yards on the northern side of the water-
shed is the Bulgarian frontier-track which we
traverse; a few yards to the southern, the Greek
track, and all along the line these explosive nations
watch each other from little hill-top blockhouses
placed alternately on either side. The path climbs
higher and higher along the ridge and the vegetation changes to something resembling our own
alpine flora. The day does not pass without a
" frontier incident." From a Greek post a big police

dog, actuated no doubt by political motives, charges
down to attack our Bulgar guard, who alone of our
company is on foot; Greek soldiers dash after him
across the frontier line in pursuit of the trans-
gressor, who is hauled off; and we proceed amid
apologies. We round a spur and see the great gable
of Karlak, heavy with forest, right in front, across a
broad wooded depression, into which we drop. The
sun is getting low when there is a splash of bright
colour among the trees, a jingle of harness, and we
are joined by Captain Damianoff of the Bulgarian
army, with two troopers; he is sent to guide us up
the mountain, and has been watching for us all
day. We are cheered to hear that by pushing on
we can reach the summit before dark, for it is rather
cold to render agreeable the idea of a night in the
open so high up among the hills. But we meet also
with a disillusionment. The maps had led us to
believe that Karlak rose to 1,900 metres. It is so
indicated on the usually correct Austrian staff map.
But maps in eastern Europe are not always right.
Captain Damianoff assures us that from his own
aneroid observations the height is 1,500 metres.
This blasts our hope of a high-alpine flora, and
accounts for the puzzling feature, observed from a
distance, that the forests run up close to the summit.
Soon we are across the intervening valley and start
the final ascent through beautiful oak woods. The
ground gets rocky and very steep, and we lead our
horses along a mere excuse for a path, over slabs of
stone and through dense thickets, and then out on
grassy shoulders gay with a hundred unfamiliar

blossoms.   A patch of vivid blue which we had noticed a couple of miles away proves to be an acre or two of a new kind of Sheep's Scabious (*Jasione*). We hurry on as the light fails, and are all well blown when we reach the military post, a half dug-out hut on the edge of the highest trees. A wash in ice-cold water and then food and a big wood fire. The soldiers spread for us on the earthen floor a bed of rare mountain flowers—surely no botanists ever had a more appropriate couch—and we sleep as best we can, with the patrols stumbling over our feet all night long as they come and go with frequent slamming of doors and blasts of frosty air.

We are up on the ridge in time for a mysterious orange sun-rise and a first survey of the mountain flora, which teems with lovely plants. Breakfast follows, of a kind of sweet Turkish pudding, unripe pears, and water. Then our ponies are mounted for the summit, a mile further on. On the steep final ridge we encounter a Greek patrol, who suggest that the path on their side is better than the one we are following, and offer to lead us. So we advance as a quite imposing cavalcade—Greek sergeant and two men in front, two foresters, two British and two Bulgar botanists; Turkish attendant, and as rear guard the Bulgarian captain and his troopers. The main summit is scaled, the soldiers fraternize and smoke under the lee of the crowning rocks, while we drink in the glorious view—northward the Bulgarian hills stretching to the horizon, southward the Greek coastal plain spread like a map, and the broad expanse of the Aegean Sea, island-studded,

with the grim ridge of Gallipoli far to the south-east.
Then we revel in flowers while we may, longing all
the time to cross to the great grey limestone crags
half a mile away; but these are in Greek territory,
and we are warned that it is inexpedient to make
ourselves the target for pot-shots from across the
valley. All too soon it is time to go, and we are led
downward by a different route, by winding paths
through miles of forest, and finally out into the
open and on to the populous village of Čakal (pronounce Chakal) where our captain has his quarters.
He and his wife entertain us right royally to lunch,
and we part from him with genuine regret, for he
has shown himself a right good fellow. The long
afternoon is spent on devious tracks over low arid
hills till we strike a great gravelly river-course, half
a mile wide, with a mere trickle of water in the
middle. Up this we go and at last cross to a Turkish
village on the northern bank. Here as elsewhere
our forester meets old friends, and we sit at coffee
with the headman, who presses us to stay and dine.
But we aim at making Daridere that night and
remount our tired beasts. Now there is actually a
well-made road under our feet, along which we
make a forced march, over a flat valley, then
through hills, finally by moonlight up a beautiful
wooded gorge. Daridere is close at hand and we
are all half asleep when suddenly round the corner
comes a motor-car with lights blazing—unprece-
dented phenomenon! Never was a quicker dis-
mounting. In a trice we are out of the saddle and
bury our horses' heads in the roadside bushes, and

the unfamiliar monster charges by without mishap.
It is near midnight when we reach our village, but
the hospitable mayor is on the look-out, and very
stiffly we mount stairs to find a smoking meal on
the table. Opining that we will be cold, the cook
has so enriched the stew with red pepper that even
our hardened Bulgars admit themselves beaten at
the third mouthful; but bread and wine and coffee
make all things right.

The morrow sees us back at M. Savoff's
hospitable camp, and after a day there the hills are
once more crossed to Ustovo; profiting by experience, we spend the night on the floor of a half-
finished house, where the only other lodgers are a
couple of goats and some hens; while our ladies,
entertained by the mayor, have an opportunity of
seeing a very beautiful Bulgarian home, and of
experiencing charming Bulgarian hospitality. Then
we are once more off by motor across Rhodope
bound for Philippopolis, but before leaving the
mountains we break our journey at the ancient
monastery of Bačkovo (pronounce Batshkovo) in
order to climb some high limestone hills in the
vicinity specially interesting to the botanist. At these
Bulgarian monasteries the old rule prevails of giving hospitality to all who ask it; but you do not
stay more than three days, and on leaving you are
allowed (and expected) to make a gift towards the
monastery funds. We find the abbot, a man famous
for his learning, superintending building operations
at the main gate, through which one gets glimpses
of a great courtyard, its centre occupied by a church

whose walls are covered, as is usual here, with
brightly-coloured frescoes with innumerable figures
of men, angels, and devils. The abbot bends a lowering brow—there is no room: he cannot take us in.
We present a letter of recommendation from the
headquarters of the church in Sofia. He holds it
between finger and thumb—he has no use for high
officials; and he resumes his architectural cogita-
tions, while our letter flutters to the ground. Our
Bulgar friends, undismayed, lead us to a pleasant
lawn adjoining the gate, where there are benches
and tables under the trees, and a wide prospect of
mountain and valley. An hour passes; then the
abbot reappears, and stiffly questions us as to
whence we come and who we are. He unbends a
little before he goes. Another interval, and he
reappears, accompanied by a tall monk with a
great red beard and streaming hair, by whom we
are courteously addressed in English. The new-
comer has spent two years at Oxford studying the
organisation and policy of the Anglican church, at
the bidding of his superiors; and is interested in
our journeyings. The tension relaxes, and we learn
that rooms may be forthcoming. Another hour and
we are summoned to a formal reception. The
abbot, accompanied by the monastery officials,
receives us in a handsome wainscotted room at the
end of a long balcony. We are duly presented;
cognac and then vodka are served: and we are
invited to sup with the abbot at eight. We are
shown our room close by, but the ladies lodge in a
special house outside the monastery walls. Supper

passes off pleasantly: the company consists of the abbot, our Oxford friend, and our six selves. It is a strict fast day, but a dish of eggs is added to the vegetable menu for our delectation. As the meal concludes, a remarkable procession passes across the room—monks bearing new mattresses, new blankets, snow-white sheets and pillows. These, we are informed, are for the ladies—fresh out of store, brand new, inviting sound repose. But, alas! on the wainscot just opposite, a creature is seen hurrying across—the writing on the wall! All the new bedding is laid sumptuously on ancient palliasses... In the men's room, in spite of plenty of napthaline, it is judged wiser to sleep in our clothes ...At sunrise we are off for the limestone peaks —up a wooded valley and on through rocks. A tall curving precipice is surmounted by a ladder-like trail of built-up blocks. Higher, the route lies up a semi-cliff densely clothed with scrub—very difficult ground to traverse. But we climb four thousand feet in five hours, and emerge on a cliff-walled plateau, a paradise for the botanist, with rare Kabschia saxifrages in masses on the rocks and a wealth of other lovely plants, among which we revel for a while. Then down again at a rapid pace to the monastery, where a motor is waiting, and we charge tempestuously over deep ruts and through blinding dust, past the gorge and out across the wide plain to Philippopolis, where incongruously we sup in a crowded smart restaurant to jazz music. Midnight sees us once more in a train, and next morning we are back in Sofia, where the joy of a bath after ten days in our clothes is one of those things that is beyond the power of language to express.

LIFE AND THE UNIVERSE.

A LITTLE time ago, writing of Sir James Jeans' book, *The Universe Around Us,* I endeavoured, by a mere consideration of dimensions, to convey some idea of that extraordinary complex of millions upon millions of whizzing stars, each composed of millions upon millions of whizzing atoms, in the midst of which we live our sedate lives. To thinking Man, interest in the Universe unquestionably centres in the problem of his own relations to it, whether in the metaphysical or the physical sense. And on the physical side, the human problem is bound up with the larger question of Life in the Universe. Let us try to get into perspective the facts relating to this matter. As to Space: so far as we know certainly, life is confined to this Earth. As to Time, the geologists suggest some three hundred million years back as the period when the Earth became fit for life, though naturally enough the earliest remains of living things which have been preserved in the rocks are not nearly so old as this. As to other conditions requisite to life as we know it or can conceive it, it is confined to a range of temperature of about thirty degrees centigrade, the lower limit being a little above the freezing point of water: the necessary materials out of which living matter is built up must be present—carbon, nitrogen, oxygen, hydrogen, and small quantities of potassium, sodium, phosphorus, and so on: a supply of free water is also essential.   On the Earth, in the presence of a sufficiency of these in assimilable condition, plant-life flourishes, and upon these plants all animals support themselves, directly or indirectly.

Now let us suppose that one of A.E's disembodied or unembodied beings, with a biological bent, came to the Universe, seeking to study the phenomenon we call Life. His first impression, as he roamed through billions of billions of miles, would be of the extraordinary emptiness and coldness of space. But at length a speck of light would lead him to one of the diffused masses of matter, which, to the number of millions, are scattered through space. And suppose that by good fortune he struck that particular agglomeration of matter, the Galaxy, of which our Sun is one of some hundred or two hundred thousand million stars, spaced out many millions of millions of miles apart, and blazing furiously at temperatures of anywhere from thousands to millions of degrees.   And if among these millions of stars he happened upon our Sun, he might discover that certain minute extraordinarily cold bodies —the planets—revolve around it.   It seems quite unlikely that even if he had examined tens of thousands of other suns he would have seen planets before.   Planets appear to be a very rare phenomenon in the Universe.   The modern theory that they are formed not by the over-rapid rotation of a star (as was formerly believed) but by the passing of two stars extremely close to each other, requires an occasion which, it can be demonstrated, is one of extraordinary rarity.   Eagerly our visitor would seek for life on the planets which wheel round our Sun. Mercury he may pass by—one side of it is always turned towards the Sun, and hopelessly hot; the other side, always turned away from the Sun is hopelessly cold. Venus would seem a more suitable abode for life: observation suggests conditions resembling those of a damp green-house under the dense clouds which cover its surface: but recent researches point to so exceedingly small an amount of oxygen in the atmosphere of Venus that animal life, as we know it, would be impossible. Moreover, during the long day that prevails there (lasting several weeks) the surface becomes extremely hot, and during the corresponding long night excessively cold. What about Mars, concerning which we hear so much? On Mars there is very little heat, very little water-vapour, very little oxygen. Arrhenius' picture of the surface of that planet is of vast deserts and frozen salt seas, with large polar ice-caps. Jeans suggests that the seasonal changes of colour that have been ascribed by some to vegetation may only be rains watering the deserts; and the evidence on which many believers in Martian life largely rely —the famous canals—he dismisses with the remark that they disappear when looked at through a really large telescope, and do not survive the test of being photographed. Arrhenius suggests that very lowly forms of plant life are the most that can be hoped for on our red neighbour. The planets which lie beyond Mars are all extremely cold, and no help comes from them. It seems possible then that our transcendental explorer would return to our Earth as being the only speck of matter in the whole Universe on which there is found what we call Life —that is, animate matter founded on a basis of water, carbohydrates, and proteins.

So much for the question of SPACE. How about life, and in particular human life, in regard to TIME? The stars of our Galaxy are regarded as being somewhere about five to ten millions of millions of years old. Behind that stretches an immense period during which they condensed from a great nebula which in turn arose out of some sort of hypothetical primeval uniform cloud filling space. Our Sun is estimated as not over 8 million million years old. Very late in its life—only about 2 thousand million years ago (or two minutes ago if the Sun's age be reckoned as one year)—there occurred that narrow escape from collision between the Sun and another star which resulted in the formation of the planets. The Earth was born as a great sphere of glowing gas which took a long time to cool and condense; but when about six-sevenths of the time intervening between the Earth's birth and the present had elapsed, the surface had cooled sufficiently to render it possible that life could appear— that is, the coldest parts were not much hotter than the hottest parts are to-day. Life, then, began, we do not know how nor where nor in what form (but probably in a guise of which the minute unicellular algæ of our ponds and seas are the nearest surviving analogue). And in ever-varying and ever-ascending form, both vegetable and animal, life had filled sea and land for many millions of years before MAN appeared, one of the latest comers of all, perhaps 300,000 years ago. During only the last one-hundredth part of his sojourn here has he attempted to unravel the mysteries of time and space, and to determine his place in the Universe which surrounds him; during only the last ten generations has he been able, through the invention of the telescope and spectroscope, to probe further than the naked eye allows.

Then in addition there is the question of ENERGY. The essential characteristic of life is its display of purposeful energy—energy of growth, energy of movement. This energy we cannot manufacture, but we receive it from the Sun in the form of heat and light, and absorb it either directly, or bottled in the form of food or fuel, and convert it to our own purposes. If we absorb too little direct energy we shall freeze: if too much, we shall frizzle. If we assimilate too little bottled energy we starve: if too much, we have indigestion. The question of temperature is indeed all-important, and, as has been seen, governs every enquiry regarding the distribution of life. Space is very vast and very cold, very thinly populated by stars which have, in comparison with our experience on the Earth, enormously high temperatures. The scale of temperature known to science runs from absolute zero ($-273°C.$, where all the clockwork of the Universe stops) to some 40 or 50 millions of degrees in the interior of the stars —according to a recent hypothesis much more still. The range of temperature at which life is possible is seen to be very small, and extremely close to the bottom of the scale. Only in a few tiny cast-off and burnt-out fragments of matter like our Earth is such a temperature found.

And what of the future? The Sun, like the stars of which it is one, is now very old. Its life is far advanced and its end is near as compared with its beginning. The exchange of energy among the stars, and the radiation of energy into space, have gone a long way towards producing that inevitable state of equilibrium which means death. " Energy cannot run downhill for ever, and, like the clock-weight, must touch bottom at last." But with millions of millions of years still to go, this approaching end does not enter into human problems, in which a mere thousand years is an age. The Earth, it would appear, will probably continue habitable for a period perhaps three thousand times longer than that which has elapsed since life first appeared upon it —three million times as long as man's present sojourn on this planet. Slowly the Sun's heat will diminish, slowly the Earth will draw further away from this source of all life : but so gradually that by human standards no change will be observed. And what changes will even a fraction of that immense period bring forth in the teeming mysterious life of our Earth? If the past foreshadows the future, all things will change again and again. No organisms, and least of all the highest, have persisted for even a considerable part of the three hundred million years of the habitable Earth. In tens of thousands of different forms, species and families have appeared, only to disappear again. Kingdoms have arisen only to fall. The great groups of the Horsetails and

Club-mosses among plants, the Reptiles among animals, have dominated the world in their day, but have made place for other and more advanced groups. At present the vegetable and animal worlds are dominated respectively by Flowering Plants and by Man. Will these also give way in their turn to something higher, and so pass progressively towards some far-off divine event to which the whole creation moves; or will Life, even as it has ascended ever since the Earth became habitable, eventually descend as the Sun's heat diminishes, and cease at length among lowly organisms such as those with which it began?